Forest Farming

If by means of forest farming world production of foodstuffs and raw materials can be increased substantially and, where appropriate, tree crops linked with industrial development, something of real significance will have been achieved – both for the better sustenance of mankind and for the preservation and enhancement of our environment.

Forest Farming

TOWARDS A SOLUTION TO PROBLEMS OF WORLD
HUNGER AND CONSERVATION

J. Sholto Douglas & Robert A. de J. Hart

WITH A PREFACE BY
E. F. SCHUMACHER

WATKINS
London & Dulverton

ISBN 0 7224 0142 6

First published 1976
Revised Edition 1980

Printed in Great Britain by
A. Wheaton & Co. Ltd., Exeter

TO MY FATHER

Odin and his two brothers soon turned their attention
to Earth. There was much about Earth that was
beautiful, and much that they loved. So they set a ring
around the planet, out of which grew the magic tree
Yggdrasil, which, by spreading its branches over the
world held it safe for the coming of man. Thus the
Sibyl's Vision says:

> I know a tree, called Yggdrasil,
> tall tree and sacred,
> sprinkled with white clay,
> thence come the dews,
> that fall in the dales;
> it stands ever green,
> over Destiny's spring.
>   (*From the ancient Norse Sagas*)

J.S.D.

Contents

List of Figures

Foreword

BY E. F. SCHUMACHER

Ten years or so ago I received, most unexpectedly, a letter from America, sent by Richard B. Gregg. It couldn't ·be *the* Richard Gregg, friend of Gandhi and author of a number of books which I had read with great benefit to myself? Well, it was. The letter was very simple. It said: 'Gandhi used to say: "When you cannot make constructive use of your books any more, give them to someone who can". I am an old man and cannot do much any more. I have looked through my library and have picked out a number of books which will be more use to you than they are to me now. May they help you in your work,' – or words to that effect. A few weeks later, a book parcel arrived and there they were, exceptional books, marvellous books, books which I should never have found myself (except for people like Richard Gregg!). Among them was one with the title *Tree Crops – A Permanent Agriculture*, by J. Russell Smith. (See p. 35 below.)

I confess, I did not read this one right away. Its subject seemed to me too remote and, I admit it, too improbable. But eventually I did read it, and it made so much sense to me that I have never been the same since. *It made sense*, because it did not merely state that 'civilised man has marched across the face of the earth and left a desert in his footprints' – a remark I had found confirmed in innumerable places throughout the world; no, it did much more than that: it showed what could be done and what should be done. Most improbably (as it seemed to me) the answer had been there all the time and was still available to us: Agriculture is for the plains, while silviculture is for the hills and mountains. When the plough invades the hills and mountains it destroys the land. . . . Just as efficient agriculture depends on human ingenuity and work – in finding the best methods of cultivation, in plant breeding, and so forth – so an efficient silviculture depends on just the same kind of effort. Without the effort, nothing much can happen.

J. Russell Smith's book made a tremendous impression on me. His assertion –

'Therefore, the crop-yielding tree offers the best medium for extending agriculture to hills, to steep places, to rocky places, and to the lands where rainfall is deficient. New trees yielding annual crops need to be created for use on these four types of land.'

As my work took me all over the world, everywhere I could *see* it, thanks to Russell Smith: Agriculture in mountainous, rocky, or dry regions is a disaster, but trees are salvation. And 'trees yielding annual crops' did not have to be *created*; they existed already. But care and attention, selection and plant breeding, the application of methodical science, could improve them beyond our imagination.

Who was there to take up the challenge? I did not find many. As I am not directly involved in these matters, I may have missed important developments. I followed the rediscovery of ecological forestry in Germany. But I was fascinated more than by anything else, with the work of Mr P. A. Yeomans of Sydney, Australia, (see pp. 138ff) whose Keyline System seemed to me to possess the perfect beauty of truth.

This book, in my layman's opinion, bringing all these matters up to date and completing them, does the one thing that can be done: It makes a viable future visible in the present. It is a book about THE GENEROUS EARTH. There is incredible generosity in the *potentialities* of Nature. We only have to discover and utilise them.

All my life has been a journey of discovery of *the generosity of nature*. I started out thinking that we had to do everything ourselves and, of course, we couldn't. But then I discovered that everything will be done for us, provided only that we realise our 'nothingness' and thereupon start to search for a way fitting-in with the great processes of Nature, and making the best of them, for our purposes.

Travelling through India, I came to the conclusion that there was no salvation for India except through TREES. I advised my Indian friends as follows:

'The Good Lord has not disinherited any of his children and as far as India is concerned he has given her a variety of trees, unsurpassed anywhere in the world. There are trees for almost all human needs. One of the greatest teachers of India was the Buddha who included in his teaching the obligation of every good Buddhist that he should plant and see to the establishment of one tree at least every five years. As long as this was observed, the whole large area of India was covered with trees, free of dust, with plenty of water, plenty of shade, plenty of food and materials. Just imagine you could establish an ideology which made it obligatory for every able-bodied person in India, man, woman, and child, to do that little thing – to plant and see to the establishment of *one tree a year*, five years running. This, in a five-year period, would give you 2,000 million established trees. Anyone can work it out on the back of an envelope that the economic value of such an enterprise, intelligently conducted, would be greater than anything that has ever been promised by any of India's five-year plans. It could be done without a penny of foreign aid; there is no problem of savings and investment. It would produce foodstuffs, fibres, building material, shade, water, almost anything that man really needs.'

Finally, as a 'fuel economist', I should like to say this: Since fossil fuels, the mainstay of the 'modern system', have ceased to be cheap and may soon cease to be plentiful, many people are becoming interested in *solar energy*. They are looking for all sorts of wonderful man-made contrivances to collect solar energy. I am not sure that they always appreciate the fact that a most marvellous, three-dimensional, incredibly efficient contrivance already exists, more wonderful than anything man can make – the TREE. Agriculture collects solar energy two-dimensionally; but silviculture collects it three-dimensionally. This, surely, is 'the wave of the future'.

I do not think the authors of this book overstate their case when they say:

'Of the world's surface, only eight to ten per cent is at present used for food production. . . . With the aid of trees, at least three quarters of the earth could supply human needs, not only of food but of clothing, fuel, shelter and other basic products.'

And they do not fail to add that wild life could be conserved, pollution decreased, and the beauty of many landscapes enhanced. This is the way, or at least one of the ways, to spiritual, moral, and cultural regeneration.

Introduction

Trees constitute one of mankind's most important assets and play a vital part in the maintenance of our environment. Indeed without them life on our planet could not survive. At the same time, forests can contribute appreciably to world food supplies provided proper exploitation, combined with satisfactory conservation, is carried out. Moreover trees can flourish and yield abundantly in many places where arable crops and field grains would fail to grow.

This book discusses the role of forests and tree crops in farming and offers detailed advice and information on various economic species, the use of their products for food and raw materials, planting techniques and suggestions and guidance for the layout and operation of schemes of forest farming. The aim of the work is to encourage the adoption of multiple-usage methods and to foster the integration of forestry with farming to form one pattern of agri-silviculture, wherever this may be appropriate.

Farmers and foresters often find it difficult to obtain adequate information and advice on economic trees and shrubs for agri-silviculture in convenient and consolidated form. This book is intended to meet the need for a handy reference and working manual. It has been written simply, but it contains enough technical material to serve the purposes of agriculturalists and foresters in all countries and conditions, and seeks to provide useful guidance and practical instructions for extension workers, planners, government departments, institutions concerned with development and research, and indeed all those interested in tree-growing, whether they be laymen or professionals.

It is hoped that this work may be especially valuable to the developing nations in whose territories exist vast stretches of virtually uncultivated and desert or wasted lands, as well as to the more advanced countries where great areas of presently marginal value still lie neglected or require reclamation for economic use. If, by means of forest farming, world production of foodstuffs and raw materials can be increased substantially and, where appropriate, tree crops linked with industrial development, something of real significance will have been achieved, both for the better sustenance of mankind and for the preservation and enhancement of our environment.

J. SHOLTO DOUGLAS

I
Re-vitalising the Rural Areas

THE MOST urgent task facing mankind today is to find a comprehensive solution to the problems of hunger and malnutrition, with all the disease and misery that they involve, by methods that do not overburden stocks of non-renewable resources, such as oil and minerals used for fertilisers, and do not impoverish the environment.

Vast areas of the world which are at present unproductive or under-productive – savannahs and virgin grasslands, jungles and marshes, barren uplands and rough grazings, deserts and farmlands abandoned owing to erosion – could be brought to life and made more hospitable to human settlement. The know-how exists to make abundant contributions to man's food needs by methods combining scientific and technological research with traditional husbandry. The 'tool' with the greatest potentials for feeding men and animals, for regenerating the soil, for restoring water-systems, for controlling floods and droughts, for creating more benevolent micro-climates and more comfortable and stimulating living conditions for humanity, is the tree.

Of the world's surface, only eight to ten per cent is at present used for food production. Pioneer agriculturists and scientists have demonstrated the feasibility of growing food-yielding trees in the most unlikely locations – rocky mountainsides and deserts with an annual rainfall of only two to four inches. With the aid of trees, at least three quarters of the earth could supply human needs, not only of food but of clothing, fuel, shelter and other basic products. At the same time wild-life could be conserved, pollution decreased, and the beauty of many landscapes enhanced, with consequent moral, spiritual and cultural benefits.

The world's two greatest under-developed resources are the human capacities for creative fulfilment, which are thwarted by hunger, poverty, disease, violence and lack of educational opportunity, and the mineral-rich subsoils which can most efficiently be utilised by the powerful, questing roots of trees and other perennial plants.

The tree is a tool of almost unlimited versatility, the use of which does not, in general, involve technical skills beyond the capacity of the average human being. It can be grown in the form of extensive orchards or forests for the production of fruit, nuts and other edible and non-edible crops, or in the form of vast shelterbelts for the containment and reclamation of deserts. On the other hand, it can also be grown in small stands by the individual farmer or gardener who wishes to attain a measure of self-sufficiency.

The world food crisis is a problem which affects, actually or potentially, every human being on earth. Its solution depends, not only on governments and international agencies, but on the efforts and initiatives of millions of private individuals.

The production of essential foods by conventional methods of land-use is lagging so far behind the needs of the world's rapidly growing population that even the advanced, industrialised, food-exporting countries are facing shortages of nutritional factors that are vital for all-round positive health. The toll of disease in the affluent countries which can be attributed to diet deficiences or toxic elements in food or the environment is becoming comparable to the suffering caused by sheer malnutrition in the poorer countries. There are comparatively few people on earth whose health and happiness could not be enhanced if they had access to a comprehensive, balanced, natural diet consisting largely of fresh products eaten direct from soil or tree.

Imagination and boldness will be required to bring into profitable bearing the huge neglected and unexploited regions that now cover some three quarters of the land surface of the earth.

Apart from the fertile farmlands, the rest of the world's inhabitable rural areas, considered from the standpoint of their contributions to food and raw-material supplies, are used at the moment simply for pastoral or low-density ranching activities, conventional forestry or orcharding, and various enterprises which contribute only marginally to the nourishment of the human race. In addition, some of these activities are notoriously inefficient in land-use, output and operation.

The comprehensive answer to the problem of these 'delinquent landscapes', as a leading farmer and forester graphically described them, is to incorporate them into integrated schemes of land-use, scientifically worked out to accord with soil and climatic factors. One of the most important factors in such schemes should be massive tree-plantings, for trees can provide food and shelter for human beings, livestock and crops and provide timber and other products for building, fuel and industry; they can heal erosion and control the movements of water in the soil; they can purify polluted atmospheres and generally conserve the environment.

By such schemes the standards of living and nutrition of millions of deprived people throughout the world could be improved and assured.

The organisers of the International Biological Programme, the operational phase of which began in 1967, stated: 'The rapidly increasing human population and the wide extent of malnutrition call for greatly increased food production coupled with rational management of natural resources. This can be achieved only on the basis of scientific knowledge, which, in many fields of biology and in many parts of the world, is at present wholly inadequate. This is particularly noticeable as far as trees and tree-crops are concerned.'

Many crop-yielding trees and shrubs are currently ignored by farmers, who allow the harvests of these plants to go to waste. With the right methods and rational management, these very same plants could form a vital segment of modern agriculture and industry.

At present, agriculture in most parts of the world is virtually exclusively geared to cereal growing and/or livestock rearing by conventional means. Cereals, such as wheat, barley, rye, oats, millet, sorghum, maize and rice, as well as annual leguminous crops, such as soya beans, which constitute the staple diet of most of the world's races, demand annual cultivations which are enormously expensive in labour or machinery, require large inputs of water and fertilisers, and are extremely vulnerable to the vagaries of the weather. Harvest failures, due to drought, flood or storm, can lead to disaster and even wholesale starvation in the affected areas.

Livestock rearing in its traditional form, as still carried on in most countries – dependent on a few strains of grass and clover and often on low-grade pastures – is an extremely unproductive type of food-production, and can also be disastrous when grazing areas are attacked by flood or drought. Through over-grazing, many regions, especially in the Sahel–Sudan zone of Africa, are degenerating into desert, and the very existence of many nomadic tribes is threatened with extinction. The exposure of bare soil, when pastures are eaten to the roots by flocks and herds and also when land is ploughed for the production of cereals and annual vegetables, frequently leads to wind erosion, while rain and sun, especially in tropical areas, leach valuable minerals from the earth.

In the wealthier countries, livestock production, whether by traditional methods or modern factory-farming systems, constitutes a serious drain on world stocks of cereals and protein, which are desperately needed for direct feeding to human beings. A large proportion of the protein incorporated in compound feeding-stuffs for animals in Western countries comes from Asia, Africa and Latin America, where millions of human beings suffer from protein malnutrition.

The rocketing price of oil and the scarcity of fertilisers, both oil-based and from natural mineral sources, constitute a further threat to nutritional standards in the poorer countries, especially those that depend largely on cereals for their basic foods. The 'Green Revolution' – the breeding of high-yielding, hybrid cereals, especially wheat and rice – which was heralded in the sixties as foreshadowing the end of the world food problem, has proved a disastrous failure in countries that have found themselves unable to afford the enormous fertiliser inputs that the new varieties demand. Moreover, the new varieties also demand vast quantities 'of water and are therefore extremely vulnerable to the ever-present threat of monsoon failure in tropical areas.

In the light of the conspicuous failure of conventional agriculture to fulfil the nutritional needs of the world's rapidly growing population, far-sighted agronomists in many countries are turning their attention to the numerous advantages of tree crops.

First and foremost, trees offer the possibility of far higher food yields per acre. Whereas livestock rearing in temperate regions produces an average of about two hundredweight of meat per acre and cereal growing an average of about one and a half tons per acre, apple trees can yield at least seven tons per acre, while leguminous, bean-bearing trees, such as the honey locust, can provide fifteen to twenty tons of cereal-equivalent. In tropical areas, and under conditions of multiple cropping – where trees are interplanted with vines, vegetables or cereals – far higher yields can be expected.

Here are some examples of fair average annual yields obtainable from well managed plantations of good-quality trees:

SPECIES	ANNUAL YIELD (Tons per acre)	REMARKS
African locust beans	10–15	Under cultivation in Malaya and parts of Africa.
Algarobas	15–20	Under cultivation in India, Argentina, Hawaii, and other areas
Carob	18–20	Well cared-for plantings in California, the Mediterranean, Middle East, and similar regions
Honey locust	15–20	Selected plantings in North America
Mulberries	8–10	Superior strains, with long fruiting season
Persimmons	5–7	Selected species and cultivars
Chestnuts	7–11	Grafted stock under cultivation in United States and France
Walnuts	10–15	European, Asiatic, and other selected cultivars
Oaks	10–12	Very variable according to species and season, but best results noted in Portugal, north of South America, North America, and Korea
Pecans	9–11	Improved orchards in North America
Olives	3–4	High-quality strains
Hazelnuts	9–12	Selected cultivars under proper management
Dates	4–7	Good, well cared-for plantations in warm dry climates with adequate ground water

Advocates of factory farming or synthetic food manufacture might claim that by such means still higher productivity can be achieved than by tree cropping. But it must be realised that extensive acreages of cereals and protein crops, such as soya beans and linseed, are required to feed battery-hens and battery-calves, while the synthetic proteins with which scientists have been experimenting demand large quantities of oil or coal – non-renewable resources which are becoming increasingly expensive and are urgently needed for other purposes.

Moreover the nutritional value of the products of factory farming and synthetic manufacture have frequently been questioned, whereas the nutritional factors obtainable from the fruits, nuts, seeds and beans of trees are mostly of the highest quality. As a 'machine' for supplying the necessary factors for sustaining human and animal life, the tree, with its deep, ever-questing roots, seeking out the riches of the subsoil, and its mass of foliage high in the air, utilising atmospheric minerals and solar radiation by the scientific process of photosynthesis, is far more efficient than any system devised by man.

Another outstanding advantage enjoyed by trees is that they can tolerate conditions in which every other form of food production would be impossible, such as steep, rocky mountainsides. Both olives and carobs, for example, can be planted in the clefts of rocks where no soil at all is apparent; their roots will penetrate deep into the heart of a hillside until they find the nutritional elements they require.

The ability of trees to tap deep underground water-veins is a supreme asset in many of the world's arid areas. Certain trees have roots which can penetrate as much as several hundred feet into the subsoil and rocky sub-strata in their search for subterranean water. Drought-resistant trees such as the almond can survive and flourish in apparently waterless conditions where all other crops fail. With their capacity for storing water for long periods, some species of trees and shrubs can survive extended droughts that kill all other forms of vegetable life. Moreover the water drawn up by tree roots from the depths of the earth can also benefit their vegetable neighbours. Tree plantations are able to raise the entire water-table over a wide area, thus bringing the

possibilities of conventional agriculture and horticulture to regions where such activities had been considered out of the question.

The water taken up by trees from the subsoil is transpired into
the atmosphere and falls as rain. The ecologist with Richard St
Barbe Baker's Sahara University Expedition discovered that a
single eucalyptus tree forty feet high transpired eighty gallons of
water a day. Tree plantations also attract rain clouds and cause
them to shed their loads, so that extensive tree growing can make
a substantial contribution to the annual rainfall of a drought-
ridden area. Trees require far less in the way of elaborate irrigation schemes than do cereals and reduce the necessity for such
schemes in neighbouring crops.

Trees can be found which will tolerate both the rarified air of
great heights and the polluted atmosphere of industrial cities. In
recent years, apple orchards have been established at heights of
over 12,000 feet in Tibet, while J. Russell Smith, the American
authority on tree crops, reported that, in the early years of this
century, a honey locust had been seen bearing its long pods in
foggy London. Better than any other crop, trees could supply the
younger generation's demand for self-sufficiency. Many suburban
areas could produce more food than open countryside stocked or
cropped according to the conditions of orthodox agriculture if the
full tree-growing potentialities of private gardens were exploited.

These facts suggest an answer to the world food crisis which
can be applied to every part of the earth where trees will grow
and animals exist; it is capable of operation on the smallest or
the largest scale; it is far less demanding in energy, machinery
and irrigation than conventional agriculture, and far from damaging the environment, it conserves and improves both soil and
water resources and purifies the atmosphere.

This is the creation of balanced, ecological plant-and-animal
communities, scientifically adapted to local climatic and soil conditions, and with species carefully selected for their favourable
relationships with each other.

In the 1930's Toyohiko Kagawa, the Japanese Christian evan-
gelist, trade-union leader, sociologist, psychologist and novelist –
a man of extraordinary versatility and deep compassion for

human suffering who will surely come to be recognised as one of the outstanding personalities of the twentieth century – became concerned about the plight of Japanese hill farmers whose soil had been eroded as a result of de-forestation. Having read J. Russell Smith's book *Tree Crops – A Permanent Agriculture*, Kagawa recognised the necessity for restoring tree cover, and, as conservation with ordinary trees does not yield early cash returns, he suggested the extensive planting of walnuts, the nuts to be used for the feeding of pigs, which could be sold as a source of cash income for the farmers. Kagawa's ideas were carried out on an extensive scale and the system became known as 'forest farming' or 'three-dimensional forestry', the three dimensions being conservation, tree crops and livestock.

Following the war Kagawa's work began to arouse interest outside Japan, and in 1956-7 the concept of three-dimensional forestry was included in an experimental scheme for developing the semi-arid area of the middle Limpopo valley in South Africa. Two types of drought-resistant trees were selected, the carob and algaroba, both of which yield large crops of edible beans which, when ground into meal, are excellent for cattle fodder and also for human food. Later, further work with tree crops was initiated at several places in central and eastern Africa, extensive experiments, combined with large-scale plantings, confirming the possibilities of the new agri-silvicultural concept.

The general pattern of three-dimensional forestry is to have large belts or blocks of economic trees interspersed with narrower grazing strips of grasses or other herbage along which move herds of livestock, fed from the woodlands, and producing meat, milk, eggs, wool and other items. The system forms a natural biological cycle, into which man fits perfectly: he can eat the food harvested from the trees and the flesh or produce of the forest-fed livestock, or sell them. The manure of the animals is returned to the soil and encourages healthy and vigorous growth of plants, thus reducing the need for bought-in fertilisers to a minimum.

Three-dimensional forestry offers more than a system for satisfying man's basic needs of food, fuel and other essentials. It offers nothing less than a new way of life, which could provide rewarding and purposeful occupations for large populations. The drift of rural dwellers to the towns is fostering excessive urban expansion in many parts of the world, and leading to the mushrooming of shanty towns with their deplorable living conditions. By offering new schemes of land development the influx into the cities could be checked, and new, vital rural civilisations and cultures created. People could return to the countryside to participate in agri-silvicultural activities which could provide profitable and meaningful occupations for thousands of workless individuals and families. Forest farming would provide many highly skilled jobs which could give the ambitious, technically-minded young men and women of today status and satisfaction at least equivalent to any available to the industrial worker, and carried out in far more pleasant and healthy surroundings.

E. F. Schumacher, in a speech in 1966, said: 'The central economic task of mankind, at this juncture, is to build up an efficient and satisfactory way of life in the rural areas, to achieve an agro-industrial structure which conquers rural unemployment, stops rural decay, and arrests the seemingly irresistible drift of destitute people from the countryside into the big cities, already overcrowded and rapidly becoming unmanageable.' Forest farming could make a considerable contribution to the fulfilment of this aim.

2

Trees and Man

SINCE THE earliest times man has maintained a love–hate relationship with his greatest natural benefactor, the tree. It is almost certain that *homo sapiens* first appeared in a 'natural orchard' environment, such as still exists in a few favoured areas today, which provided both shelter and the food which was most conducive to the development of his higher faculties. Like his nearest relative, the anthropoid ape, which has greater strength for its size than any other animal, primitive man must have subsisted very largely on the fruit, nuts, shoots and leaves of the trees among which he lived. There is, in fact, anatomical evidence that man is intended by nature to be fruitarian. A special affinity appears to exist between the most advanced forms of animal and vegetable life. But mankind has from time to time indulged in orgies of destruction of his original forest home, leading to erosion, desiccation of the soil, the advance of deserts and even the disappearance of whole civilisations.

Plato described this unhappy process. At one time, he wrote in the *Critias*, there were great forests on the mountains of Attica. 'Moreover there were tall cultivated trees in abundance, and the mountains afforded pasture for countless herds.' But many severe storms occurred, and the soil was swilled away from the higher regions and lost at the bottom of the sea, '. . . so that what is now left . . . compared with what existed then is like the bones of a body wasted with disease : the fertile soil has fallen away, leaving only the skeleton of the land'.

The Athenians thus, like other nations before and since, were faced with the challenge of an eroded landscape, due undoubtedly to hillside tree-felling. But, unlike other peoples who merely abandoned their ancestral lands and moved elsewhere, the Athenians faced boldly up to the challenge and overcame it. They turned away from stock-breeding and grain growing, the staple pursuits of Greece in that age, and concentrated on the cultivation of the olive and the vine, both of which can grow and even flourish on denuded slopes. And on these, together with silver and pottery of the highest artistic standard, made from veins of high-quality clay exposed by the process of erosion, they founded the prosperity of the Athenian empire.

A similar saga – one covering millennia and fulfilled only in our own day – has unfolded in another Mediterranean land, Palestine. In ancient times the mountains of Palestine and Lebanon supported dense virgin forests, which supplied timber for the empires of Egypt and Mesopotamia. Among cultivated trees, the olive, the fig and the date were of the greatest economic importance. The Bible relates that John the Baptist survived in the desert by eating 'locusts and honey'. The word 'locusts' here means 'locust beans', according to modern scriptural authorities. These are the edible fruits of the wild carob tree, and it is likely that they were also the 'husks' eaten by the Prodigal Son. Clearly, therefore, carob-pods were used for animal feeding, as they are – in enormous quantities – today. As late as the tenth century A.D., despite constant wars, an Arab traveller mentioned carobs, together with olives, dried figs and raisins, among Palestinian exports, and spoke of the 'luscious fruits' of Ramleh, the 'enormous grapes and incomparable quinces' of Jerusalem and the 'apple orchards of Hebron'. But in the following centuries devastation set in. Under the Crusaders the 'enchanted forest' of the Vale of Sharon was cut down; later invading Arabs laid waste villages together with their orchards and vineyards, and under the Ottoman empire a heavy tax was imposed on every tree, and in desperation many *fellaheen* resorted to cutting down their trees in order to avoid the tax. The destruction of tree cover was practically completed in the early nineteenth century when the country was overrun by vast herds of goats belonging to Arab nomads.

Towards the end of the nineteenth century and the beginning of the present century the first pioneer agricultural colonies were established by Zionist immigrants, and these set about the restoration of the land, using trees among their principal implements of reclamation. Watersheds were heavily forested to halt erosion and restore subterranean water supplies; hillsides were terraced

and planted with olives, vines, carobs and fruit trees; malarial
marshes were drained with the aid of eucalyptus trees imported
from Australia, and the citrus industry was introduced. During
the last war, when exports of oranges and grapefruit were interrupted, Palestinian scientists discovered various uses for the un-
sold fruit, including the feeding of orange pulp to dairy cattle.
At the present time, the prosperity of the state of Israel owes
much to the country's perennial agriculture and horticulture,
and Israeli scientists are engaged in important research into desert
reclamation by tree planting.

In the Far East, national prosperity has long been associated
with an abundance of economic trees. Boasting of his country's
wealth, a thirteenth-century king of Siam said: 'Coconut, jack-
fruit, mango and tamarind abound in this land. Whoever plants
them, unto him they shall belong.' It was under a Bhodi tree –
believed to have been a drought-resistant fig – that the Buddha
attained enlightenment, and he enjoined on his followers that
each one should plant at least one tree every five years and tend
it until it was firmly established. Commenting on this precept,
Dr E. F. Schumacher writes in his book *Small is Beautiful* (Blond
& Briggs, London, p. 205): 'As long as this was observed, the
whole large area of India was covered with trees, free of dust,
with plenty of water, plenty of shade, plenty of food and materials. Just imagine you could establish an ideology which would
make it obligatory for every able-bodied person in India, man,
woman and child, to do that little thing – to plant and see to the
establishment of one tree a year, five years running. This, in a
five-year period, would give you two thousand million established
trees . . . The economic value of such an enterprise, intelligently
conducted, would be greater than anything that has ever been
promised by any of India's five-year plans. It could be done without a penny of foreign aid; there is no problem of savings and
investment. It would produce foodstuffs, fibres, building material, shade, water, almost anything that man really needs.'

In Europe, the fundamental importance of the tree to mankind
was symbolised by the sacred tree, Yggdrasil, of the Norse sagas,
which was said to have kept the earth safe for the coming of the
human race. Edible pinenuts, processed into a tasty flour, were a

common article of diet in the legions of imperial Rome, particularly among soldiers stationed in outlying or frontier regions,
such as Hadrian's Wall in north Britain. Excavations undertaken
in the ruins of old Roman cities like Pompeii resulted in the discovery of dried tree fruits in abundance, notably walnuts, persimmons, dates, pinenuts and carob beans. During the Middle Ages,
vast herds of pigs and other farm animals were fed almost entirely from the acorns, walnuts, chestnuts and beech seeds produced
by the great forests that then covered most of the land. Several
economic trees were among the many plants introduced into
Europe by the Moors. Describing the countryside round Granada
under Moorish rule, Washington Irving writes in his *Conquest of
Granada*: 'The hills were clothed with orchards and vineyards,
the valleys embroidered with gardens ... Here was seen in profusion the orange, the citron, the fig and pomegranate, with great
plantations of mulberry trees, from which was produced the finest
silk. The vine clambered from tree to tree; the grapes hung in
rich clusters about the peasant's cottage.'

In both North and South America, the pods of the mesquite or
native algaroba were known to the Aztecs and the Incas as palatable and nutritious additions to the human diet and of good use
for stockfeed. Prior to the Spanish conquest in 1533 A.D., the only
noteworthy farm animal in Peru was the llama. The state herds
maintained by the government were pastured extensively on the
wild algarobas of the Andes. Oswalt,[1] writing about the food supplies of the Desert Cahuilla Indians of California, states: 'The
most important plant in the collecting activities of the Desert
Cahuilla was the mesquite tree which grew plentifully in groves
found anywhere between the desert floor and heights of up to
3,500 feet in better watered areas. The pods were not gathered in-
discriminately, for the beans from some trees were regarded as
more palatable than others. Pods could be stored from one year to
the next. They were crushed in an upright wooden mortar with a
stone or wooden pestle. Further processing included grinding up
the pods ... the meal could be placed in shallow round pottery or
in basketry containers and moistened. After drying the caked

[1] W. H. Oswalt, *A Study of the North American Indian*, University of California, Los Angeles (1966) J. Wiley & Sons Inc., New York.

meal was removed and stored. Sections of the cakes were broken off and eaten as a snack or carried by travellers as food. The meal could also be made into a gruel or soaked in water to make the mesquite juice beverage. Loose ground meal was kept for making into porridge later. The mesquite bean was the most important staple, but the people likewise gathered screw beans as a subsistence item, and of the four varieties of acorns available, those of Kelloggs oak were preferred for their taste and consistency. The capabilities of a woman were measured by her skill in leaching and grinding acorn meal. Very finely ground meal was made into cakes and baked in hot coals, while coarse meal was made into a gruel. Acorns which were not ground at the time they were gathered were stored in raised platform caches.'

African tribes, too, have for long been aware of the merits of several indigenous trees, which yield crops of beans and seeds of high value as fodder for cattle in the dry periods when grazing is scarce. But in Africa, as in other continents, there has been wholesale destruction of forests in many areas, resulting in increased desiccation and even the advance of deserts. This has partly been due to the unplanned and misguided imposition of some European and American farming practices, especially widespread monoculture, on traditional African husbandry, which, if not highly efficient, was at least generally compatible with the conservation of the environment.

All over the world, at various times and in different areas, the forests have contributed appreciably to man's subsistence and often saved whole populations from starvation. It was therefore natural in former days, and certainly until the advent of the Industrial Revolution that the woodlands should have been looked upon by people generally as useful adjuncts to the farming economy. Drawing as they did a considerable part of their daily foodstuffs from trees and being directly dependent upon forest produce to fatten the animals that they killed for meat or kept for other reasons, everybody quite rightly considered the forested areas to be complementary to the cultivated arable farms and gardens. No artificial dividing lines or barriers existed marking off into rigid limits the different features of the countryside.

Several factors, however, have combined during the past hundred years or so to destroy the self-sufficient subsistence economy of earlier times over the major part of the world. Increases in urban populations created new demands upon rural areas for extra production of grains, which could only be met by more intensive farming. The somewhat haphazard and careless gathering of forest fruits or nuts and the casual pasturing of herds and flocks in the woodlands proved quite inadequate to cope with the large requirements of the freshly created industrial communities. Society changed both in organisation and needs. While this was happening food production became specialised, breaking up into separate practices and disciplines. Forestry, which had previously been an integral and useful part of the agricultural scene, was virtually relegated to the role of supplying firewood and timber. The new town-dwellers packed into the cities and factories and cut off from rural life, came to regard the woodlands as rude and savage habitats, the haunts of wild beasts, fit only for the hunting of game, useless to progress and quite opposed in every way to the comparative civilisation of the farms.

Imbued with such ideas industrial man indulged in a further orgy of destruction, partially completing the work of his ancestors who had ruthlessly cut down and burned the once vast forests of the Sahara, the Thar, the Middle and Near East, and North Africa and turned them into barren and ruined wastelands. The new blow fell mainly in Southern and Eastern Africa (now suffering from increasing desiccation as the result of the removal of much of the local tree cover) and in the North American continent, where the notorious 'dust bowl' was created. The discarding of forestry as an integral section of agricultural production and the consequent upsetting of the balance of natural influences led inevitably to extensive soil erosion, frequent lowering of water tables, and the creation of unrivalled opportunities for the spread of plagues and epidemics.

Until quite recent years, the exclusion of forestry from farming was regarded generally as final and definite. Silviculture was looked upon by the bulk of this century's farmers as a separate technique, having no possible relevance to the growing of food. The culture of fruits had been allotted to the horticultural sphere and orchards were considered as falling into the domain of garden work. There were few contacts at scientific level between for-esters and agriculturists and virtually none in the technical or practical fields. Woodmen had withdrawn entirely from the food-production industries and held almost no communication with workers in forestry's sister disciplines. Such a state of affairs had most deleterious effects upon the whole applied science of silvi-culture and greatly retarded its development and its contribution towards the feeding of the world's peoples.

3

Ecological Cultivation

THE NATURAL ecological climax for most parts of the world where more than one type of tree will grow is the mixed forest. This is the most productive and healthy form of land-use and the one most beneficial to the soil and other factors in the environment, including man. As trees exhale oxygen, the forest has been called 'Nature's lung', and in conservationist circles much concern has been expressed that the wholesale destruction of forests, such as is proceeding in the Amazon basin, may lead to a reduction of atmospheric oxygen below what is essential for the world's human and animal population. The well-known forester, Richard St Barbe Baker, who founded the Men of the Trees Society in 1922, has stated that for minimum safety a country should have about thirty per cent of its surface under tree cover. In many countries tree cover is well below that figure; in Great Britain, for instance, it is six and a half per cent, while several countries in the drier parts of Africa have only a handful of trees to the acre. Some countries in the Sahel zone, where the Sahara is rapidly encroaching southward, as well as Botswana, on the edge of the Kalahari in Southern Africa, are virtually treeless.

The mixed forest is not a mere conglomeration of assorted plants, it is a highly complex system of checks and balances, adapted to the climatic and soil conditions of the area.

In Nature the diverse plant and animal species do not – nor can they – exist in isolation. The survival of each type depends upon the presence of the others. An association of plants and animals, known as a *biocoenosis*, is formed in given habitats under environmental conditions. It includes plants synthesising organic substances (producers), animals feeding on these plants (consumers), carnivores and parasites living at the expense of the consumers, and organisms capable of mineralising organic substances that create conditions favourable for plants. The proportions of the number of individuals of the various species in the biocoenosis are also mutually conditioned. These numbers are maintained in the proportions most advantageous to the biocoenosis by regulating mechanisms evolved during its historical development.

It is commonly supposed that neighbouring plants rob, each other of sunlight, air, water and soil nutrients, and that therefore economic crops must be grown in sterilised isolation, with all potential competitors ruthlessly eliminated. But, as the exuberant productivity of the tropical forest clearly indicates, cooperation is a far more potent force in Nature than competition. Much research remains to be done into the complex biochemical mechanisms by which different plants stimulate each others' growth and neutralise each others' diseases and other antagonistic factors. It is well known, for instance, that the roots of many leguminous plants contain nodules which are the habitat of bacteria with the power of fixing atmospheric nitrogen. This is liberated when the roots decay, thus enriching the soil and fertilising neighbouring plants. Other plants, such as oaks, buckwheat and nettles, accumulate large quantities of calcium which are similarly released to the benefit of the entire biocoenosis. Furthermore, a soap-like substance, called *saponin*, exists in many plants, including common vegetables such as spinach, beet, tomatoes, potatoes and runner beans, and is also released in the disintegrating process. This is one of the reasons for the effectiveness of the traditional crop rotations practised by farmers and gardeners throughout the world.

Both the biochemical elements and activities of plants and the habits and activities of the forest fauna are responsible for the complex mechanisms of biological control, by which pests and diseases are kept in check. The presence of predatory fauna helps to ensure that no one group of animals, birds or insects assumes a dominating role and attains pest proportions. Also, if the forest contains a wide variety of plants, it is probable that these include the natural food plants of potential pests, which are therefore not tempted to encroach outside their normal preserves. The reason why, in recent decades, some birds and insects, previously regarded as innocuous, have become serious pests in agricultural areas, is undoubtedly the wholesale destruction of natural plant-life which is characteristic of modern western agricultural practices. Deprived of their normal food, such birds and insects have resorted to economic crops, sometimes with devastating effect. An example of this is the invasion of English orchards by bullfinches and their destruction of fruit blossom, following the widespread bulldozing of the hedgerows which used to be a characteristic feature of the English countryside, and which harboured the wild plants which were their natural food.

Trees and other plants that are native to a particular region tend, over the millennia, to build up a very rich ecological association of birds, animals, insects, mosses and parasitic plants – far richer than exotic species, even though these may have been introduced centuries ago. An example is the ecological wealth of the aboriginal English oak, which was a constituent of the virgin forest which once covered most of the British Isles, as compared with the ecological poverty of the sycamore, which was introduced from Southern Europe in historical times. The presence of such primordial species in a forest, whether natural or man-made, is of the greatest value for biological control, and contributes to the positive health and prosperity of the whole organism.

There is also evidence that certain plants, especially those which exude aromatic scents, have a prophylactic effect on neighbouring plants; this is another region where scientific research is required.

The forest, unlike most agricultural set-ups, is a 'multi-storey' organism comprising both low-growing and high-growing trees, with canopies at different levels; light-demanding and shade-tolerant species; low shrubs, and a carpet of small plants and fungi – all co-existing harmoniously and each one making its individual contribution to the energy and productivity of the whole.

Moreover, the layering is repeated below ground; the roots of the highest trees penetrating to the deepest strata of the subsoil, those of smaller trees and bushes occupying intermediate layers, while shallow-rooting annual and perennial plants send out a mat of roots just below the surface. Minerals and other nutrients extracted from the different strata are interchanged between the various root-systems by the burrowing activities of earthworms and other soil-organisms, which also help to maintain the circulation of minerals, water, gases and sunlight by keeping open the pores in the soil. At the same time, water drawn up by the highest trees from spring-veins in the depths of the subsoil is made available to their shallower-rooted neighbours, thus assuring their survival even in times of drought. Above ground there is a similar intensity of activity, as leaves extract minerals from the atmosphere and generate energy through photosynthesis; while on the surface of the soil a continuous composting process takes place, as dead leaves mingle with other plant residues and are activated into fertility by animal droppings. The whole vast system of the forest is therefore self-watering and self-fertilising. The circulation of water-borne minerals – equivalent to the circulation of blood in the human body – feeds and energises the entire complex organism. At the same time, the action of leaves and roots has a filtering effect on rainwater, ensuring that it is absorbed gently into the soil, to be stored in underground reservoirs as an assurance against drought.

When a forest is felled or burnt, and the land ploughed up, all these advantages which benefit the surrounding landscape as well as the forest itself – are lost. The rains beat down on the bare soil, leaching its minerals, drowning its living organisms, and destroying its structure and circulatory systems. Much of the water, instead of being absorbed into the soil, is either evaporated from the surface or rushes down slopes, slashing them into erosion channels and gulleys and carrying away topsoil, which eventually finds its way into streams and rivers and out to sea. The watertable, hitherto maintained near the surface by the suction effect of the forest's multitudinous root-system, sinks deep into the subsoil, and the flow of springs, boreholes and wells diminishes, until they completely dry up.

Under tropical conditions the process is far more drastic than in temperate climates. The effect on bare soil of a tropical storm can be destructive in the extreme; most of the elements of fertility can be annihilated in a few days, after which the tropical sun beats down pitilessly, baking the earth very hard and suffocating any seeds that may have been sown. It has been erroneously suggested that the fertility of the tropical forest is 'illusory', but the truth is that its fertility disappears rapidly under the conditions of ruthless extermination that have too often been applied to it by man, in his anxiety to exploit its economic potentialities according to his own limited outlook and knowledge. On the other hand, some primitive methods, though seldom particularly efficient, do no lasting damage to the environment. Even shifting cultivation and 'slash-and-burn' techniques allow for the natural regeneration of the forest.

It is the wholesale destruction of forest cover, whether by nomadic tribes with their herds or by ancient Roman or modern African or European agriculturists with their cereal monoculture, that leads to desert conditions. Then the vast complexity of life yields to the simplicity of death.

Today, the Sahara is encroaching on the good land of Africa with ever increasing momentum. The pre-Sahara (fringes of the desert) extends from one to three hundred miles all round the desert. In this area people with primitive farming techniques struggle against drought, locusts and the poor soil left by wind and water erosion.

The Sahara spreads rather like leprosy. Little bad spots here and there go unnoticed, until suddenly the whole area is infected – unless strong preventive measures are taken.

Few people will now dispute that the Sahara was a region of forests in past times. In conjunction with probable climatic changes, a careless felling of tree cover, mostly for firewood, the introduction of goats and camels and, as the situation deteriorated, the practice of pasturing them on trees, were the main causes of present conditions. There is almost no alternative forage now except when wild flowers shoot up briefly in the desert during the spring. Goats and camels eat seedling trees and thus make natural regeneration impossible. They also consume young growth and destroy re-afforestation already done. Thus any plan for reclamation must include provision for food and forage requirements, through the planting of crop-bearing trees.

Much destruction of forests, often quite unnecessarily, has accompanied the spread of what is termed civilisation throughout the world. Typical instances of such past folly caused the barren hillsides of Greece, the degradation of Southern Italy, the arid wastes of Spain, and the ruination of the Scottish highlands. In

Peru, the ruthless and predatory *conquistadores* destroyed beyond repair the magnificent farming system of the Incas and allowed the forests maintained by the state to deteriorate into worthless scrublands.

Man has turned vast territories to tillage, but in the process he has broken up the biocoenic associations formed in the process of evolution; this has concurrently affected the self-regulation of the populations of species. These disruptive influences have spread far beyond the boundaries of the areas planted to farm crops or used as pastures and meadows for livestock. Man has thus practically taken upon himself the concern of balancing the relationships between cultivated plants and animals and their environment. A whole armoury of technical means is employed for this purpose, but unfortunately only too frequently in the blindest manner. That is why we are now faced with problems of imbalanced agriculture and crop protection, together with a worsening of environmental conditions and serious erosion.

A most urgent problem of today is the comparative geographic study of the laws governing the formation and existence of associations of species formed in connection with farming systems. These so-called *agrocoenoses* differ considerably from biocoenoses. The species constituents of the agrocoenoses are depleted and their mutual ties are of a transient nature. As a whole, this association is either devoid of self-regulating mechanisms or they are generally weakened. A thorough investigation of various agrocoenoses will make it possible to determine the possibilities of influencing their formation purposively. Such investigations will also be an aid in outlining proper ways for applying agro-technical and biological measures to achieve correct balance and active stimulation of useful species within an economic framework. There are important indications to show that tree crops and farm forestry for different purposes can make real contributions to integrated agrocoenoses, fulfilling modern requirements and conserving land health, as well as improving the environment in which we live.

In forestry circles today the most advanced opinion postulates that, in creating a shelterbelt or a wood or forest for economic or ornamental purposes, man should conform as far as possible to the ecological conditions of the region. Rolf Gardiner, a land-owner who planted three million trees on Cranborne Chase in southern England, believed that the aim of afforestation should be to approximate a region's natural ecological climax. Thereby an agrocoenosis would be formed which would be fully adapted to local soils and climatic conditions, while its constituent plants – as well as its wild-life – would possess favourable relationships with each other. A new environment would be created, with much of the diverse and abundant vitality of the primeval forest, with its natural checks and balances, its mechanisms of biological control, but consisting entirely of economic species carefully selected to perform single or multiple functions for the benefit of man.

The expression *multiple usage* as applied to forestry may be open to various interpretations. Much depends on how far the person who employs the words is prepared to go in putting them into practice. Strictly speaking, any system of tree culture which extends the scope of forest plantings beyond the normal work of supplying timber could be justifiably defined as one of multiple usage. Within this sphere of activity there will of course be numerous divergencies. The farmer who establishes a windbreak which he stocks with gamebirds, the conservationist who lays out a protective belt of trees and shrubs to guard a new irrigation dam, the owner of hill land who plants new woods to shelter his deer, the grower who creates large orchards of nut-yielding species under the open canopies of taller deciduous types that produce timber – all these are engaging in one or more forms of multiple-use forestry. Because multiple-use systems of tree cropping have run parallel to or even preceded and perhaps included in their purview the growing of tree crops for different purposes, it is essential to know exactly what their general implications are.

Mention has already been made of how, at the start of the Industrial Revolution, forestry in western and other comparable countries came to be excluded from the main body of agricultural production. Its lengthy isolation, extending until very recent times, quite understandably gave rise to a pronounced reaction amongst its workers. Indeed, of all the applied biological sciences, forestry or silviculture still remains by and large one of the most conservative in its outlook and discipline. The growing of trees for conventional or timber-producing purposes has followed circumscribed patterns and been confined within rigid limits. Suggestions made for extending the scope and purpose of forest science and practice were all too frequently dismissed as being outside the objectives of the discipline. Only quite lately have there appeared to be cracks in this barrier of indifference and immobility. The agent in effecting change has been none other than the new techniques of multiple usage. By inducing forestry to become outward-looking again and to seek fuller integration with farming and animal husbandry, rather than remain segregated, the pioneers of multiple-use systems have performed a most useful service. There is now every expectation that silviculture will once more attain to significant force in the world agricultural economy. Moreover, modern multiple-usage methods are vastly superior in their capacity for sustained output than were the old haphazard ways of silviculture. These developments represent a considerable break with ideas that have prevailed for over a century. The putting of woodland to additional productivity within the general pattern of multiple usage not only means following approved ecological principles of land health but it also brings in appreciable financial advantages. Idle forests or units devoted to monoculture frequently represent wasted resources. Unless trees can show really good profits they will eventually go the way of all uneconomic entities in this modern age.

4

The Background of Forest Farming

THE GATHERING of tree crops and the general practice of forest farming have their origins far back in history. Long before the advent of industrial states, peasants all over the world were in the habit of using the products of forests for feeding their farm livestock. Indeed, even now, in many parts of the globe this custom still continues. Seeds, nuts, pods, fruits, and also foliage obtained from trees and shrubs have constituted important elements in the economies of different lands. The earth's forests protected and nourished not only settled societies but earlier primitive man as well. Our remotest ancestors ate the fruits and nuts of forest species and relied upon the woods for shelter and raw materials. Without such sources of diet, human beings and their animals would have died from hunger at certain seasons.

Out of all the world's continents, Asia provides the largest collection of historical material concerning man's agricultural habits. Even a cursory reading of some of the old manuscripts and tablets reveals the part played by tree crops in the farming of former periods. The idea that the forests could supply food for human beings and their livestock was never quite a novelty in Asia. In Oceania, too, several species of trees have been known and appreciated by countless generations of indigenous peoples. During recent years, however, there has been a tendency to neglect and discard such crops, mainly because the introduction of foreign methods of cash or extractive farming, as well as the development of plantation industries based on monocultures, have encouraged whole populations to turn away from traditional practices.

Probably one of the most interesting developments in the field of forest farming in Asia has been the work undertaken in India recently along the eastern borders of the Thar desert. This expanse of barren and infertile land lies between the North-West Deccan and the irrigated valley of the Indus river in Pakistan.

Despite its present aridity, there is evidence to show that in former times the Thar was a comparatively well watered and prosperous region. When the Aryans entered India between 2000 and 1500 B.C., they apparently found many thriving communities already established in the area now called Rajasthan, which today includes within its boundaries most of the Thar desert. After driving out the indigenous peoples, the newcomers proceeded to cut down and destroy the woodlands that had protected and sheltered the soil for centuries. These activities resulted eventually in the loss by erosion of practically all the fertile land, so that now, after the lapse of hundreds of years of wilful neglect and improper usage, Rajasthan is more or less a sterile and worthless wilderness. Yet the state covers an area of 132,150 square miles, appreciably larger than Bengal and Bangladesh. India's population is rising rapidly and the country as a whole is still unable to produce enough food to give its inhabitants an adequate level of diet. Development of the empty wasted lands of the Thar desert could make an enormous difference and supply badly needed extra nourishment. Another danger also exists. The desert is advancing and threatening to engulf the agricultural holdings of the Jumna and Ganges valleys, especially around Delhi. To ward off this menace, a scheme of tree planting was initiated, under United Nations auspices, for the purpose of interposing a protective belt of forest, 400 miles long by two miles wide, along the eastern border of the desert. In addition to providing useful cover for the fertile lands to the east of Rajasthan and checking the spread of the sandy wastes, these woods might become eventually a starting point for the reclamation of the whole region. The bulk of the plantings have been *Prosopis* spp. (algaroba), which can yield large crops of cereal-substitutes. It is common practice in Rajasthan to use the beans or pods of algarobas to feed goats and cattle. Up till the present time, however, hardly any thought was given to the intensive cultivation of such trees for food production. The results so far secured with stands and belts of algaroba and other types of trees in the Thar have been encouraging. Bearing has commenced at from two to three years, and could no doubt be speeded up by the introduction of superior varieties.

In Western Asia, particularly the Near East, tree crops have been long regarded as of vital importance in the economy of various nations. Carobs are cultivated in Cyprus, Asia Minor, and the Syrian region, as well as in Palestine. Large quantities of beans are exported annually from these countries. The trees thrive on rocky or dry land and provided winter temperatures do not fall below −7°C, injury from cold is unlikely. The culture of *Ceratonia siliqua* has reached an advanced stage in most of the producing countries, with the harvests being fed to livestock, or else processed into manufactured goods. Rather similar in appearance to carob beans are the pods of the jering tree (*Pithecolobium jiringa*). Although indigenous to tropical America, this species was introduced into South-East Asia in the early nineteenth century. It has been grown in plantations in Malaya for the production of stockfeed. The fruits or beans are relished by cattle. Jering and related trees are quick growing and attain the greatest size in hot moist localities, but will tolerate drier districts, where in fact they maintain a more shapely form and do not become so top-heavy.

In the Pacific area and the Antipodes, Australian aborigines have for generations preserved certain species of acacias, the seeds of which they harvest and grind into meal or roast. In Polynesia, the Tahiti chestnut (*Inocarpus edulis*) provides the local populations with a staple article of diet, while the pods of *Inga* spp., are eaten commonly. Both kinds of trees are cultivated. Hawaii is noted for its extensive algaroba plantations, totalling over 50,000 acres. From these forests more than one million tons of fodder are collected annually, and considerable amounts of honey are obtained as a by-product. *Prosopis juliflora* was first introduced to the Hawaiian islands in 1828, seed being brought from the Royal Gardens in Paris.

In Afghanistan, the dried white mulberry takes the place of bread or *chapattis* in the people's diet during certain months of the year. In Syria, too, mulberries are dried in the sun and then ground into flour. Both human beings and animals relish this meal. Persimmons are an important crop in both North and South China. The fruits preserve well after dehydration and make excellent forage for farm livestock. Walnuts and chestnuts also have an essential place in the agricultural economy of several east Asian lands, notably in Japan, Siberia and on the Chinese mainland. There are numerous varieties and strains of these trees, many of which are very resistant to frost and winter cold. Nourishing meals for pigs, cattle, and other stock are prepared from the nuts.

Carob trees were first planted in California between 1870 and 1880. The local climatic conditions have suited the crop and as a result of intensive breeding programmes some very high-yielding strains have been developed. The work of Coit[1] in this field has proved most valuable: some of his varieties or cultivars produce harvests of over 1,000 pounds per tree yearly. Where about fifty trees are planted to the acre the total yield can exceed twenty tons annually. It was found that budding is essential and good budwood commands high prices. There is today a progressive and well established carob-growing industry on the west coast of the United States, turning out livestock feed and other items for general consumption.

Recently, efforts have been made to improve by selection the honey locust (*Gleditsia triacanthos*), which is native to the north American area. Good specimens of this species can give very high yields of edible pods or beans, often more than a foot in length each. In addition to the identification of superior strains, work has begun on the hybridising of the tree with types like the Siberian pea tree, a species especially tolerant of cold, and the carob and algaroba. For years, knowledgeable American farmers have planted honey locusts in their fields to supply forage for winter feed.

Algarobas may be found all over the Americas and flour or meal prepared from their pods formed the basis of the majority of aboriginal diets. Indian tribes knew and appreciated the merits of *Prosopis* spp., from Texas to Chile. There are many types of algaroba tree, the United States having six species growing within its borders and Argentina fifteen species. Both heat-loving and frost-resistant kinds are common. In some areas, like Arizona, two crops of beans a year can be gathered, the first in early July and the second at the beginning of September. Considerable work has been carried out on algaroba at the New Mexico Agricultural

---

[1] Dr J. Eliot Coit, University of California. Numerous publications on carob cultivation in California.

Experiment Station. In Argentina, the trees are often grown in irrigated plantations to supply fodder for livestock.[2]

The value of mulberries for pig feeding has been recognised for many years in the southern states of America. In North and South Carolina and Georgia, practically every pig-lot is planted with these trees. It is generally thought that one good bearing plant can support one pig during the fruiting season of at least two months. In the case of the ever-bearing varieties, Price[3] calculated that a single tree, producing from May to July, would provide for two hogs weighing one hundred pounds each and keep them in a healthy condition for that period. Trees are normally set out at between 35 and 40 to the acre. Persimmons (*Diospyros* spp.) can be used in a similar manner. They have long fruiting seasons and are eaten with relish by cattle, horses and other farm livestock, which, however, normally will not touch the leaves. There is much variation in persimmons and about two hundred species of the trees are known to exist in different parts of the world. In consequence careful choice of types is necessary.

Chestnuts have been called 'tree corn', but until the development of blight-resistant strains, production could be hazardous. Now that suitable types are available, the uses of chestnut meals or flour are being more widely appreciated by farmers. Native American chestnuts were always renowned for their delicious flavour, as well as for their rapid regenerative abilities after cutting. In fact, many varieties bear fruits even more quickly than do orchard apples. Before the European settlement of the eastern seaboard of what is now the United States, extensive forests of *Castanea dentata* covered the land from as far north as Lake Champlain down to the region of the Alabama river. The natural harvests of the trees provided the indigenous Indians with an

[2] Nourishing cattle food is harvested on a commercial basis today in North-West Peru and Bolivia from *Prosopis juliflora* and *P. tamarugo*. The Plant Production and Protective Division of the Food and Agriculture Organization of the United Nations, Rome, has drawn attention to the value of these tree crops. In the Pampeana formation and the Chaqueña sub-region of Argentina, *P. caldenia* and *P. nigra* are grown extensively for the same purpose. Projects have been sponsored by the Secretaria de Estado de Agricultura de la Nación, at San Luis.

[3] Professor J. C. C. Price, Agricultural and Mechanical College, Mississippi.

important item of diet and also furnished useful food for the early pioneers.

Another valuable crop was gathered from various oaks, some of which bear their acorns in great numbers. The nuts themselves are palatable, while the tannin in certain kinds is easily removed. In the forest regions of Texas today *Quercus* species play an essential role in the farming economy. Ness[4] has commented: 'In the eastern part of the state, acorns furnish a very important part of the pig feed. As to the classes of this feed, there are two, namely: (i) from the white oaks, that is the oaks that mature this fruit in one year and yield what is called "sweet mast", which is considered equal to the best of our cultivated grains as hog food. Among the oaks of this kind may be mentioned the post oak (*Q. minor*), because of its number and fertility, and the white oak proper (*Q. alba*), on account of its excellent quality and size of the acorns, as well as their abundance; (ii) from the black oaks (*Q. trilobata, Q. rubra,* and *Q. marylandica*) which mature the acorns in the second year after flowering. This is called the "bitter mast". It is very abundant, but is considered inferior. These five trees, when full grown, are heavy yielders. The white oaks that produce the sweet mast are especially abundant yielders of nutritive food for pigs. Where the trees are properly thinned so as to develop freely, an acre of land set with either the white oak or the post oak is equal to an acre of corn ... management would be very effective in increasing the yield. I wish to say that the possibility by proper forest management of obtaining large quantities of feed is very great. Oaks can easily furnish in the fall and throughout most of the winter, the major part of the large amount of food necessary for raising and fattening hogs. Thinning and judicious selection of good bearing trees would be a measure of high economic importance. It is not only pigs that thrive and fatten on the mast of the forest, but also goats. During the early part of the season they feed on the underbrush and sprouts from the stumps of trees and when fall comes they fatten readily on the acorns and other fruits. My personal experience is that in east Texas stock can be raised cheaper than anywhere else, provided advantage is taken of the forest. It also happens that much of the

[4] Professor H. Ness, Chief Horticulturist, Texas Experiment Station.

land covered with forest is of such nature that it cannot be readily put into cultivation, owing to the unevenness of the ground in some cases or to poor drainage in others.' Oak trees, of different species, can be found throughout the Americas. In Colombia, amongst the Cordilleras, massive stands of *Quercus* types bearing acorns over four times larger than any to be seen in northern continents grow freely.

Walnuts have for long been a commercial crop in the United States, both for animal feeding and for human requirements. There are numerous species and cultivars available, many of which will withstand winter temperatures well below zero. The nutritional value of the nuts is excellent. Furthermore, because of the deep root systems of most walnut trees and their thin open foliage, grass and herbage will grow quite satisfactorily beneath them. Another productive crop is obtained from pecan or hickory, which is cultivated in orchards east of the Mississippi river, or in meadow pastures in Oklahoma and Texas.

Southern Europe and the western and central parts of the Mediterranean sea coasts offer many old examples of established tree cropping. From ancient times, species such as the carob, the chestnuts, the oaks, various kinds of pines, walnuts, and several others have been cultivated in these regions. The contribution made throughout the ages to the economy of the whole continent and its southern neighbours has been most significant. Going as far back as the Etruscans and the Greeks of antiquity, we find that the value and uses of food-yielding trees were fully appreciated. Homer's heroes, the Spartan defenders of Thermopylae, the legionaries of Imperial Rome and the peasant peoples of medieval times – all relied to greater or lesser extent upon food supplied by forest species for a large portion of their daily nourishment. Similarly, in North Africa and on the various islands of the Mediterranean, dependence upon tree crops has always been widespread.

The passage of the years has not to any appreciable degree diminished the part played by forest produce in many areas of the Mediterranean basin, or indeed in the general agricultural programmes of certain European countries. At the present time, such crops are still regarded with considerable favour. Extensive plantations of carobs exist in Sardinia, Sicily, the Iberian peninsula,

Algeria and Tunisia and other lands. Because the carob thrives on rocky and poor-quality ground, under arid conditions, it is frequently planted on hillsides where the culture of citrus fruits would be impracticable. In France, chestnuts are included in farm cropping programmes in certain localities. Often as much as one third of a holding may be devoted to chestnut growing, the trees being spaced out on arable sections or else kept in orchards, the produce being fed to the farm livestock. For the peasants of Portugal, oaks are a valuable source of animal feed. Acorns are harvested both from the cork oak (Q. *suber*) and the evergreen oak (Q. *ilex*). The Persian walnut can be found under cultivation throughout Europe, notably in the Balkans, Greece, Italy, Spain, France and areas to the north. Some farmers plant the trees haphazardly around their fields, but there are many well cared-for orchards, from which nuts are exported to different places.

The stone pines of Italy, with their spreading rounded canopies of light green foliage, form a striking feature of the landscape in parts of that country. The reddish brown, shining and ovate cones with pyramidal scale apices are prized for their edible seeds or *pignons*. The crops obtained from *P. pinea* occupy a significant place in the local agricultural economy and Italian *pignolia* are sold in many areas of the world. Pinenuts are fairly rich in oil and pleasing to the taste. The Aleppo pine (*P. halepensis*) is native to south-eastern Europe and another species bearing edible nuts is *P. cembra*, or the Swiss stone pine, also a productive tree.

Honey locusts have been introduced into France during recent years and efforts are currently being made there to extend plantings of this important north American species. In Spain, algaroba (*Prosopis* spp.,) grows wild and is known locally as *algarrobo*. Up to the present, there appears to have been no attempt to cultivate the trees intensively. However, the suggestion has been put forward that Iberian farmers might benefit if improved strains of algaroba were to be introduced on farms, especially in regions where water is scarce, pasture practically non-existent and livestock suffer from inadequate feeding. Hazelnuts or filberts (*Corylus* spp.), of which there are eleven economic types in cultivation, are well distributed in most parts of both Northern and Southern Europe. Demand for the nuts remains good and the trees are easy to establish. Another crop of some importance is almonds, of which there are many varieties, either hard-, or soft-shelled. Excellent flours or meals can be prepared from both filberts and almonds, which are commonly grown in orchards and plantations, as well as in gardens.

There is little doubt that the planting of tree crops in different areas would today be on a much larger scale if more adequate support from official sources was forthcoming. One problem is often the shortage of good stocks of high-quality seeds and planting material. A typical example of this kind of obstacle can be found in the following quotation contained in a communication from a forestry department in Southern Africa:

'Though we have several indigenous trees which are potentially wonderful fodder species, they must first be improved by breeding and selection. The reason so little has been done is that it requires systematic and painstaking breeding work. Research work by state departments is also often hampered by shortage of both staff and funds.'[5] Yet, West[6] has pointed out that the intensive planting of selected native fodder trees in the savannah areas of the African continent could revolutionise livestock farming within a decade. Similarly, when Neilson[7] wished to hybridise the honey locust with the Siberian peatree (*Caragana arborescens*) in order to produce a new species tolerant of extremely cold winter weather, the United States Department of Agriculture informed him that money for the experimental work was then unobtainable.

While in certain cases, breeding and selection of superior cultivars may take a lengthy period, in other instances this is not so. By choosing the best types from natural stands it is often possible to develop a higher yielding strain within a comparatively short time. In 1956-7, J. S. D. selected vigorous, heavy cropping, thornless algaroba types in Hawaii for introduction into the Limpopo

[5] Private communication from the Department of Forestry, Pretoria, Transvaal.

[6] Dr O. West. Pamphlet No 1520 of 1950, Ministry of Agriculture, Salisbury, Southern Rhodesia.

[7] Professor J. Neilson, Department of Horticulture, Fort Hope, Ontario.

valley in Southern Africa. The progeny of these trees were also thornless, as well as quick growing. The seed collected after the first pods developed was of excellent germination percentage. Second-generation crops were flourishing in the Limpopo valley within four years.

When danger threatens an established industry, resources can generally be found to ward off total disaster. The Federal Government saved chestnut growing in North America from the devastating effects of blight by introducing and distributing several thousand trees of Chinese varieties, many of which were hybridised with indigenous kinds to produce disease-resistant types. How much better it would be if governments all over the world were to sponsor intensive schemes of tree-crop improvement and selective breeding as part of an international effort to multiply superior strains of high-yielding forest species. Such a project would at long last bring ample supplies of first-class tree seed and planting or grafting material within the reach of all farmers and do for tree crops what the work of plant breeders has already done for cereals and vegetables.

5
What is Forest Farming?

THE FIRST suggestion by a modern Western scientist that large-scale tree-growing, other than in the form of conventional orcharding or viticulture, might make a substantial contribution to human and animal nutrition came in 1929. In that year J. Russell Smith, Emeritus Professor of Economic Geography at Columbia University, published his epoch-making work *Tree Crops – A Permanent Agriculture*. This book put forward the thesis that certain crop-yielding trees could provide useful substitutes for cereals in animal feeding programmes, as well as conserving the environment.

Smith's arguments were based upon his observations in a number of different countries. The example of Corsica was noted. There are in that island large stands or orchards of chestnut trees, which yield annually harvests of food for men and beasts. For centuries countless Corsican families have supported themselves by gathering these nuts, while the presence of the chestnut forests has ensured that the land is protected from erosion. In contrast to conditions in Corsica, the circumstances prevailing in West China, when Smith visited the country early in the century, seemed all the more shocking. There the hillsides had been ploughed and left treeless. As a result huge areas of formerly fertile soil had been lost irretrievably. Yet both the Mediterranean island and the provinces ruled by Peking are mainly mountainous regions, with similar problems and needs. 'Why then,' asked Smith, 'are the hills of West China ruined, while the hills of Corsica are, by comparison, an enduring Eden?' The answer to him was plain. China had been destroyed by the spoliation of her forests, but Corsica had been saved by the practice of a tree-cropping type of agriculture. Other instances served to reinforce this view. Tree species such as carobs, honey locusts, walnuts, mulberries, hickory or pecans, and persimmons were known to produce valuable yields of beans, nuts and fruits which can be dried and processed into meal or flour. Could not these additional types be grown and used in the same way that chestnuts were? It should be possible to obtain superior high-quality cultivars by selective breeding programmes and skilled planting. This would make the incorporation of forests or big orchards of such kinds of trees an essential part of agricultural development projects and a source of profit and advantage to farmers. To meet what he rightly felt was a vital need, Smith proposed the progressive establishment of massive complexes of tree farms. In his own words he saw a future of 'a million hills green with crop-yielding trees and a million neat farm homes snuggled in the hills. The hills of my vision have farming that fits them and replaces the poor pasture, the gullies, and the abandoned lands that characterise today so large a part of our country [United States of America]. These ideal farms have their level and gently sloping land protected by terraces . . . their other parts are planted with crop trees – mulberries, persimmons, honey locust, grafted black walnut, grafted heartnut, hickory, oak, and similar harvest yielding species. There is better grass beneath these trees than covers the hills today. The crops are worked out into series to make good farm economy.' In addition to advocating widespread changes in patterns of national agriculture and forestry, Smith also formulated certain rules of procedure. He recommended the reclamation of steep unploughable lands and the afforestation of rough pastures as well as the development of what he termed a 'two-storey agriculture' designed to enable farmers to grow tree crops in combination with raising livestock, the produce of the trees being fed regularly to the animals.

Shortly after Smith's book on tree crops had been issued it was read by Kagawa in Japan. He decided to experiment with the new methods and adapt them in detail to local conditions, with the object of providing peasants farming on degraded hill lands with alternative means of livelihood. Much of the Japanese mountain areas had been denuded of forest for timber and fuel cutting purposes and the sale of woods for furniture making and ship building. Once deprived of their natural protection, the hill lands began to erode rapidly and large amounts of the scanty covering of soil were being washed away. Kagawa was keenly alive to this danger and quite apart from the purpose behind the schemes of improving the standards of the farmers, he saw the need for conservation measures. As conservation with ordinary trees yields no immediate cash returns, he endeavoured to sweeten the rather bitter pill with a sugar coating of early profits. The technique he employed called for the extensive planting of walnuts, using the nuts for feeding pigs, which were then sold as a source of cash income. When plantations eventually matured, the scheme encompassed the sale of timber and replanting, so that ultimately there would be a continuous succession of economic cropping, combined with regular profits for the smallholders. Kagawa's trials and subsequent extension work were quite satisfactory and showed that the system offered a sound basis for the utilisation of tree products as fodder for livestock. These experiments and demonstrations represented a distinct reversal of previous agricultural and woodland policies, current since the industrialisation of Japan, which then conformed to common world practices and favoured the segregation of forests from farms. The trials showed that the planned integration of economic tree species with commercial livestock had very considerable possibilities.

It was obvious that the promise and practical results of the initial trials and demonstrations in Japan, conducted under severe and testing conditions and not without many technical difficulties, were sufficient to justify further extension work both locally and in other countries. But contrary to what has so frequently occurred in the case of some startling or revolutionary methods, little publicity was given to this potentially important and novel system of forest farming, nor was much general encouragement forthcoming. The results achieved remained largely unknown to the outside world. This may well have been because few scientific workers then realised exactly what the new concept involved or appreciated its value. The idea did not then become widespread that forest farming could have a profound effect upon the national economies of states or on the agrarian communities of backward regions. Indeed, the use of the concept as a means of changing the social life of rural areas and its possibilities as an aid in the profitable development of unproductive or marginal lands were more or less ignored by the great majority of orthodox foresters and agriculturists. Also, within a short space of time the world war of 1939-45 intervened; Japan became an active participant in the conflict from 1941 onwards and communications with scientists in other areas were interrupted for several years. Although limited work continued on forest farming, the new applied science and practice of agri-silviculture was overlooked and relegated to virtual obscurity for the duration of the war. Not until 1946, when the world gradually returned to some semblance of order, was it possible to reopen contacts and exchange scientific information. The work undertaken in Japan on forest farming at last attracted some outside attention of the kind that it deserved.

From the mid-1950s to the late 1960s the joint author, J. S. D., undertook development programmes using forest species in southern Africa, with the object of assessing the responses and value of economic tree crops in new conditions. The research and field studies were planned and executed in collaboration with Dr H. Boyko, chairman of the International Commission for Applied Ecology and president of the World Academy of Art and Science, Rehovoth, Israel, and in cooperation with Unesco.

In 1956-7 the concept of three-dimensional forestry was included in an experimental scheme for the development of the semi-arid area of the middle Limpopo valley north of the Zoutspansberg hills. This was a backward region of the hot summer-rainfall *lowveld*, typical of the southern African scrub savannahs. It carries a bush type of vegetation, with some medium-sized trees. The dominant species there is the mopane (*Copaifera mopane*), a drought-resistant, resinous tree, which seeds and regenerates freely. The average height of the mopane seldom exceeds thirty feet, but in areas of heavier rainfull it can grow up to sixty feet tall. During the dry winter, the leaves of the mopane provide a valuable supplementary cattle feed, but are considered to give rise to slight taint in the milk of dairy cows consuming them and other drawbacks are that the trees use up practically all the soil moisture, so inhibiting the growth and spread of the natural grasses. A tree of some interest from the picturesque point of view, also found in the valley districts, is the baobab (*Adansonia digitata*). It is now a protected species, and the same applies to the marula, which yields fruits suitable for jam making and containing edible nuts of delicious flavour. These seeds can be crushed to obtain an oil of high quality for culinary purposes. The water table generally varies from between thirty to one hundred feet. There is ample evidence of extensive underground sources of water, but in the dry season this is frequently saline. Nevertheless, it is quite good for irrigation, although it could give rise to soil-salinity problems were it ever to be used without due care or over prolonged periods for horticultural cropping. There is virtually no intensive farming in the middle Limpopo area.

About fifty years ago, the valley floor on both sides of the Limpopo river supported a wide variety of herbivorous big game, including elephants. There is evidence that the bulk of the smaller streams, now dry except in the wet seasons, used to contain running water at all times. Civilised man's advent into these districts, which occurred just after the conquest of the Matabele kingdom by Cecil Rhodes in 1893, has resulted in a general deterioration of the natural conditions, mostly as the result of mining, improper pastoral practices, indiscriminate cutting and clearing of bush trees and shrubs for fuel and other purposes, and until very recently, the absence of any conservation programme.

Two kinds of drought-resistant economic trees were chosen for initial testing, namely, the algaroba or mesquite (*Prosopis juliflora*), and the carob (*Ceratonia siliqua*), both leguminous species. Good algaroba varieties or cultivars can yield up to twenty tons of edible beans per acre annually. The meal is an excellent cereal-substitute, superior to common field grains in nutritional content. The carob is well known and of accepted utilitarian value.

The algaroba seeds were selected in Hawaii from proved high-yielding stock, while the carob beans were obtained in Cyprus and from Paris. The latter were grown as rootstocks, budding material being imported from Californian orchards. Propagation of seeds took place in nursery beds, protected by matting shades against excessive sun scorch. Algaroba seeds are sometimes difficult to germinate, due to the hard testa or outer coat, and to secure the best results, they were scalded with boiling water and soaked overnight before sowing. When about six inches high the young seedlings were transplanted into small grass baskets or containers, made locally, and removed to an open section of the nur-

sery. Watering was provided as necessary, and the plants grown
on till they had reached a height of some eighteen inches. They
were then judged fit for planting out in the arboreta and field
stands. To prepare the final growing sites the existing scrub had
been cut down to ankle level and treated with suitable arboricides
so that the introduced exotics would be able to develop free from
active competition by uneconomic native species. The young
algaroba trees were set out twenty-five feet apart in cleared contour strips, use being made of planting holes excavated to a depth
of up to two feet. The entire root system of each young tree, still
within its original container was placed in its individual hole and
the soil raked back round it and pressed down fairly firmly. The
first plantings were made in December to January 1957-8, during
the summer rainy season. Growth was rapid, and at sixteen
months the trees were in flower, with pods appearing. By the end
of eighteen to twenty months after setting out the initial harvests
were ready for collection. Thereafter, production increased year
by year, as the trees grew and matured. The best Hawaiian algaroba varieties are thornless, which assists the work of picking the
produce considerably.

The carobs were treated in a similar manner, but great care had
to be taken in setting the young seedlings in longer containers
since any exposure of or disturbance to the taproot causes death
of the plants. Transplanting was in consequence done when the
seedlings were some two inches high and a ball of soil or compost
was left around the roots. The containers into which they were
moved were longer to accommodate the rapidly developing taproots. After the trees had attained a height of two to three feet
they were budded while still in the nursery and later planted out
in prepared holes thirty feet apart in the cleared forest strips,
without any root disturbance being permitted. This meant that
the containers, with the sides and bottoms slit open to allow the
roots to enter the soil freely, were lowered into the holes in a
single operation. In order to have budwood available locally when
required an earlier importation had been arranged for from California, and the stock trees had been established in containers at
the horticultural station in Pretoria. It was then a simple matter
to collect material for grafting as needed. Budding itself is a

straightforward horticultural task, easily done with polythene strips. The carobs began bearing small crops at four years, thereafter steadily improving their output.

Both the algaroba and the carob established themselves well in the Limpopo valley areas. The initial plantings were followed by others, so that it was possible to build up a successional series of belts and blocks. Once the young trees had rooted, growth continued unimpeded, and it was merely necessary to keep down any regeneration of the native bush until the foliage of the exotics provided effective overshading and secured dominance of the sites in question.

In addition to the two species already mentioned certain other types of trees were planted, on different sites. These included the Japanese honey locust (*Gleditsia japonica*), also a leguminous species, which produces edible pods or beans; various *Acacias* noted for their useful seeds which can be ground into palatable meals for livestock feeding; African locust beans of *Parkia* spp., well known as providers of famine food in the form of large pods and seeds with especially high protein content; and Tallow trees (*Detarium senegalense*) of the savannah varieties. These last named yield fruits suitable for drying, and the seeds which contain oil may be eaten, or the oil extracted by pressure and the residue employed as livestock feed. In all cases the propagation techniques used were similar and included sowing of seed in nursery beds followed by transplanting into small baskets or other suitable containers for an adequate period to allow the development of strong and vigorous root systems and then transfer into field conditions within normal belts or blocks of afforestation. The distances and spacing were adjusted to the estimated growth capacity and eventual size of the species in question.

Further field plantings undertaken in different areas during recent years have included the true honey locust (*Gleditsia triacanthos*) and the Mexican hawthorns (*Crataegus* spp.). In the Shire valley rain and jering trees (*Pithecolobium* spp.) appeared to be well suited to the warm conditions. The thick sugary pods of these species are very nutritious and are much liked by cattle. In the Sibiti valley, which is situated south of the salt-water lake Eyasi in east Africa, forming part of the Rift system, the soils are variable and there is flooding and waterlogging in some places, but areas of lighter loam exist, with a water table of fifteen to twenty feet. Under such conditions the carob tree responded satisfactorily, since the valley temperatures rise to 40°C in summer. Above the valley, to the east, is the cooler Iramba plateau which reaches heights of just over 5,000 feet above sea level. On this tableland a range of exotics, including the honey locust, certain types of sweet chestnuts (*Castanea* spp.,) the Mexican hawthorn, and various kinds of pinenuts, were selected for testing. Propagation practices followed normal routine and several arboreta and field plantings were carried out, with rewarding results. All these different species responded well to local climatic conditions. The Uluguru mountains (maximum elevation 9,697 feet) in eastern Tanzania are situated about a hundred and twenty miles inland from the seaport town of Dar es Salaam. The surrounding district is largely devoted to sisal growing and is warm and dry with a rainy season lasting from December to April. This provides adequate moisture to encourage sufficiently vigorous rooting by tree species to tap underground water supplies quickly and so enables them to survive the months of drought without difficulty. Amongst the by-products of the sisal plant (*Agave sisalana*) is a quantity of succulent material which can be processed into livestock feed. If appropriate tree species are interspersed throughout estate plantings and crops of cereal-substitutes harvested from them, the combination of these two forages will contribute to the good health and output of dairy herds. The sisal then becomes a ground crop thriving under an open canopy of carob, algaroba, or other suitable types of trees.

It has been found that when clearance of scrub has been completed, the growth of local grass and herbage species often doubles within a single season. Such indigenous grasses are normally fully adapted to the local environments and only need minimum care and attention to realise their potential. Once free of severe competition from taller overshading shrubs and trees, rapid development of pasturage will occur. To supplement the output of grazing strips, various useful plants such as the salt bushes (*Atriplex* spp.,) *Polygonum* spp., and similar herbage types, as well as appropriate high-quality grasses of proved strains, may be introduced when necessary. The species chosen should depend upon the places concerned and the local climatic and related factors.

From this outline of the development of forest farming it will be clear that the aim of the system is to increase and diversify the productive capacity of woodlands, so that, instead of only timber and connected items, their output should also include a wide range of foodstuffs and other raw materials. Agri-silviculture, in its broadest sense, defines all plant culture and livestock keeping as parts of one whole biological cycle, looking upon each farm unit as a progressing entity. Forestry is integrated with farming, animal husbandry and horticulture to achieve both maximum output and optimum conservation of a given area.

When the system is fully applied in practice it becomes three-dimensional, comprising as it does three major items: first, the trees, valuable in themselves as sources of timber, as conservers of the land against erosion, and as factors in some climatic amelioration; second, the harvests yielded by the trees which serve to nourish and fatten commercial types of livestock; and, third, the animals living around and among the trees and feeding off their produce, which become available for sale as meat or else supply milk, butter, cheese and eggs, as well as other useful goods. There are thus three benefits to be derived from this new system of cropping rather than the single one normally obtained from ordinary farming or forest exploitation. Added to these, there is a secondary output, which includes hides and skins, wool, honey from ancillary apiculture, gum in some districts, timber, charcoal, hay and silage. This list is by no means exhaustive. In emergencies the cereal-substitutes produced by the trees may be used for human food.

This kind of layout calls for the creation of large belts or blocks of economic trees interspersed with narrower grazing strips of grasses or herbage along which move herds of livestock, fed from the woodlands and producing meat and other items. The cereal-substitutes harvested from the trees, supplemented by the pasturage, support the animals. The system forms a natural biological cycle into which man fits perfectly; he can eat the food harvested from the trees and the flesh or produce of the forest-fed livestock. The manure of the animals is returned directly to the land and

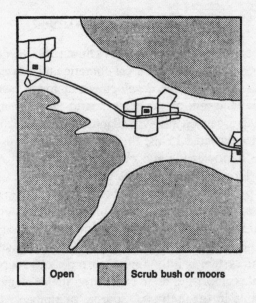

| | Open | | Scrub bush or moors |

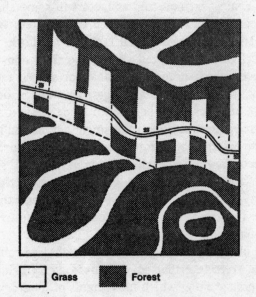

| | Grass | | Forest |

Fig 1. Changes in land usage brought about by the introduction of forest farming

I. Before: conventional land pattern with arable farms growing field crops confined to small patches of better soil. Balance scrub grazing

II. After: agri-silviculture layout with planned tree crops producing cereal-substitutes plus pasture strips encourages healthy and vigorous growth of plants. Culture of this type may be introduced in places where orthodox farming or forestry would be impracticable or uneconomic. There are no expensive field operations or heavy capital outlay on machinery. Labour needs are very low and moreover the burden of general work is lightened.

The three-dimensional concept has been designed to conform to ecological principles and practice. Each forest farm is intended to constitute a local ecosystem which has been imposed upon a previously barren or unproductive area, or substituted for hitherto unprofitable existing agricultural or silvicultural holdings. In fact, the technique should preserve and improve the ecology of regions, and it aims to bring into being virtually self-supporting units of production.

Three-dimensional forestry achieves a synthesis of farming, tree growing and animal husbandry: they do not just complement one another but become a single integrated whole. Unlike the medieval or traditional peasant methods of forest utilisation which were haphazard and unscientific, modern forest-farming activities are intensive and well planned and they have to be capable of adjusting to a wide variety of conditions according to the demands of specific environments.

Forest farming has as its fundamental purpose the offering of one complete and integrated applied science instead of the conventional separation of silviculture from agriculture – a cleavage, which, by the way, is unknown to Nature. Excessive specialisation in agriculture and dependence on monocultures have already inflicted great damage upon different regions of the world by interfering disastrously with the ecological balance to the detriment of its inhabitants. Tree cropping practices may redress to a considerable extent the obvious defects of orthodox farming and forestry which impede their effective use in areas where local conditions are too exacting for the extension of conventional methods. This possibilty of forest farming surviving in regions where ordinary cultural practices would stand no chance of success is a matter of importance. Marginal lands occupy a high percentage of the earth's surface. At the present time, most of them are lying idle and derelict. The widespread introduction of tree

crops might go a long way towards developing many currently
useless jungles, moors, scrub savannahs or thorn bush, stony or
sandy deserts, and what are so often ambiguously called 'rough
grazing' areas. A further advantage of farming with trees is the
general simplicity of operation, provided that the broad principles are followed and the proper methods are applied.

6

Designing a Forest Farm

THE PLANTING and culture of trees is, of course, a longer term project than the year-to-year programmes of most arable farming. Nevertheless, by using high-quality, selected and quick-growing cultivars or varieties of suitable tree species, yields may be obtained quite speedily. The choice of species depends on their adaptability to the conditions in question and their produce. Trees may be grown in plantations or orchards and groves on flat land, or in long contour strips for hilly and undulating ground. Often belts of open pasture or herbage may run between and separate the stands of forest trees. Up to the time that bearing begins, which in some cases may be only two or three years, farmers could get partial returns from the grass on the land for fodder and animal food or else they can raise certain other annual crops while the trees grow tall. In certain instances, the yields of tree crops from mature plantations have been as much as twenty tons per acre annually.

The space available for tree harvests offers far wider scope for output than can be afforded by the spread of field grains. This is because their bearing area is not merely horizontal but also vertical: the contrast is that between a square and a cube. This increase of fruiting area, combined with rooting systems penetrating the subsoil and underlying rock strata, can give tree crops considerable advantages over shallow-rooted cereals and vegetables. Cropping tends to be not only more abundant, but also more reliable, as trees are far better able to stand up to drought, flood and other adverse conditions than are annual crops, and by careful pruning it is possible to ensure consistent harvests.

All tree-growing projects require careful preparation, and in the cases of large-scale schemes detailed preliminary investigations should be carried out on the proposed sites. Before commencing field operations, it is desirable to undertake a proper survey of the areas to be planted. The object of such studies is to collect all the relevant information about a locality and its crop-yielding potential. By doing this beforehand, much saving of time and avoidance of waste of resources may be expected, while haphazard procedures are eliminated. After the collection of information and its appraisal, practical work can proceed smoothly. Since one of the aims of tree planting is progressive improvement of the environment, full details of the potential of any selected areas is vital in order to succeed and there is no substitute for adequate and reliable information.

A convenient form of survey is given at the end of this chapter. By following the procedure laid down, farmers or foresters can assemble a useful body of knowledge about the conditions prevailing on the land, as well as the economic possibilities of tree growing and so acquire a good guide to which lines of development may be best for forest farming. Much of the information can probably be obtained from maps, local records, meteorological charts and general soil and aerial surveys. Statistics in production and marketing are also relevant. The factors bearing on new developments which concern farmers closely are those of climate, physiography and biology. Rainfall, atmospheric humidity, wind, temperature, and light will all be most significant. There is evidence to support the view that tree planting improves poor climates or mitigates their adverse effects. Physiographic influences, such as elevation, slope, waterlogging, deposition, erosion and denudation and related matters have their origins in the natural formation of the earth. Then there are the the edaphic or soil factors, including mineral content, mechanical composition, organic material, acidity, soil water and aeration, as well as the consideration of the soil as a developing entity. Biotic influences are created by the activities of living organisms – plants, animals and man himself. All these living forces exert their own effects in different ways.

PLANS AND THEIR PREPARATION

Once the collection of information has been completed and the initial survey carried out, the actual planning of the forest farm

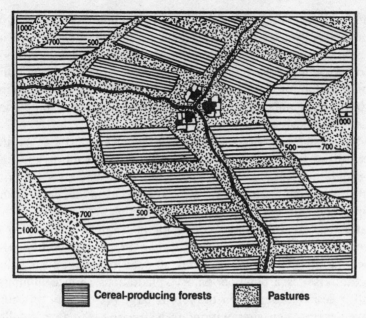

Cereal-producing forests   Pastures

Fig 2. Section of forest-farm layout

Note the rectangular blocks of trees on flat valley lands and the contour-aligned belts in the hilly sections

can begin. Several alternative types of appraisals may be employed, but the basis for any scheme is the preparation of a map. This can be quite simple, even in the style of a sketch for small projects, though it is usually easiest to obtain standard sheets covering the area. Often, government-survey maps show a considerable amount of local detail, and if aerial photographs are available these can be of much assistance. Mark out on the map or sketch the boundaries of the land and trace the main features, including hills, valleys, rivers and streams, marshes, lakes or sandy flats if these are not already shown, in clear outline. Insert reference points and heights above sea level where necessary. Once all this has been done, you will have a fairly clear idea of the general distribution of the important localities on the proposed farm, or in the case of places intended for reclamation, of the sites that need attention.

By using the map you have prepared in combination with the

information contained in the form of preliminary survey, you can build up a comprehensive plan for the development or rehabilitation of the chosen area that conforms to these guidelines. Certain vital needs must always be kept in mind: maximum conservation of soil and water, protection against prevailing winds, optimum safeguards from erosion and provision of good access to all sections.

Experience has shown that it is advantageous to employ the focal-point technique in new developments. This means that the forest farmer selects one or more sites possessing such facilities as actual or potential water sources, convenience of ingress and egress and adjacent expansion zones, in other words, all the attributes that are commonly looked for in a centre of operations. From nuclei like these, extension can proceed smoothly. The focal points will contain a series of small complexes, including forest nurseries, arboreta or embryo plantations, service buildings, and if desired, housing on the job. A large project will probably have several such sites within its boundaries, but in a smaller scheme there need only be one, or at the most two focal points. The positioning of these centres should be done with due care,

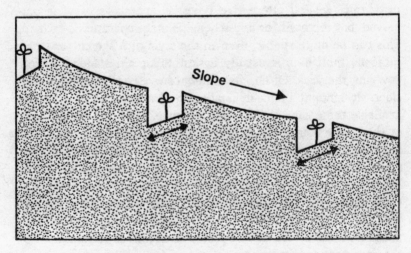

Fig 3. Trench or *banquette* system
Side view of *banquettes* or shallow trenches with inclined bottoms

since they will constitute a sort of combined advance guard and headquarters for the transformation of the land.

An overall land-usage plan should also be prepared. This is marked initially on the map, and must show in the case of large schemes the placement of the forest blocks and belts, the lines to be followed by any interspersed grazing or herbage strips, the access roads and tracks, and such essential facilities as watering points, storage areas, and other necessary or supporting installations. Plantations may be arranged in square or rectangular style on flat or very gently sloping ground, or else in any convenient shapes to suit particular needs.

On hilly or undulating lands, it is essential to plan for belts aligned along the contours. These can be of considerable length, provided breaks and access tracks are introduced at appropriate intervals. Wherever practicable, use should be made of check dams, *banquettes* or trenches for moisture conservation, tilting or staggering of blocks of trees to give shelter from excessive wind, drainage ditches, and other aids to effective land planning. No two areas are exactly the same, however, and each one is likely to require its own individual development scheme.

Laying Out

The next step is to mark out on the ground itself the boundaries of the forest blocks and belts and the interspersed grazing strips, as well as the sites of the supporting facilities that have been entered upon the working drawings. To accomplish these tasks successfully some knowledge of simple map reading is necessary, as well as ability to use a levelling instrument. The level is employed for correct alignment of the forest belts, so that surface run-off of water and erosion are eliminated. It is important that the belts should be properly spaced out at stated vertical intervals on hillsides, with the directional lines horizontal, otherwise heavy rains will wash away topsoil and cause gullies and scars to form, thus destroying fertile land. By marking on the field maps the approximate positions of the eventual plantations, farmers and foresters will be able to take a particular contour as the base line and work from it. The boundaries of sections are marked by short posts, painted white for ease of recognition and driven into the ground at appropriate distances from one another. If the marking out is clear and accurate, much time will be saved later when planting starts.

Before finalizing any programme for tree cropping the economic aspects of the plans must be carefully considered. It would be utterly useless to develop a series of new crops in a region where there was little demand for them, or from which there was no possibility of profitable export. The question of costs is vital. Markets should be scrutinised at the beginning of any preliminary investigation, and careful estimates formulated to discover if the capital outlay on development will bring in satisfactory returns. The assessment will include tentative expenditure and gross profits, together with anticipated net income as the scheme progresses. All plans should be flexible and capable of modification and adaptation, as need arises, or for novel and exceptional circumstances. Remember, you are dealing with biological material, not just machinery of a static nature. The work of establishment may be said to be progressive and continuous: no scheme of applied biological scientific intent can ever be complete in itself or at rest.

Layout must be designed to achieve optimum output. One of the main advantages of forest farming is that this type of culture, once established, should give a high return with no expensive field operations or outlay on machinery and it may be introduced in places where orthodox forestry or arable cropping would be impracticable. For ranching areas, too, the technique has distinct value, being more likely to be profitable than the customary habits of using paddocks or grazing stock over vast stretches of poor-quality grassland, known in different countries under the names of ranges, veld or outback.

The tree crops may be arranged in orchard style on flat ground, that is spaced out preferably in quincunx or alternate manner, with grass cover between individual trees, or in long contour-aligned strips for hilly and undulating areas, or else in squares and rectangles. In all cases, belts of open pasture or herbage can be sited to separate the plantations. The best average width for belts and blocks of forest is about 300 yards, but any convenient length can be employed. The interspersed open strips should be

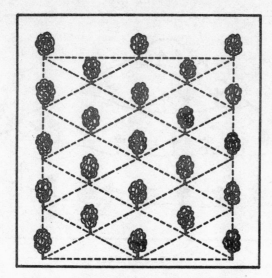

Fig 4. Quincunx pattern of planting
An alternate method normally recommended for tree crops

on the average some 50 to 100 yards wide. These distances allow for good production combined with easy field management and simplify general work programmes. However, some variation is permissible in exceptional cases.

Contour-aligned belts can stretch for many miles and make a most impressive sight, as they wind around and along hillsides. In flatter parts, the blocks are best kept to a length of not over half a mile. It may be practicable in some places to introduce a secondary layer of low trees or shrubs underneath the main species, if the upper canopy remains open enough to admit some light. In exposed sites, it is often advisable to plant lines of guard trees along the edges of plantations to check strong winds. Owing to the nature of hilly or undulating ground, it will of course be obvious that the width of belts and strips cannot be constant throughout their length. Some variation and increase or decrease must occur according to the horizontal direction of the contour lines. Though slight inconvenience may arise in calculating the exact number of trees to a belt, this is amply compensated for by the complete prevention of erosion and the excellent conservation of moisture that the contour planting provides.

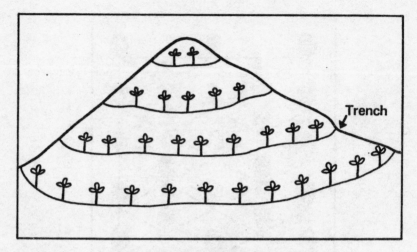

Fig 5. Contour alignment on hills

The first task in laying out forest farms is to transfer from the planning map or sketch on to the ground the proper boundaries of the plantations and the open strips. At the same time, in big schemes, the sites for nurseries, water points, buildings, assembly points, and other essential facilities must be marked out. Traces should also be cut for roads of access and here care is necessary to ensure that these are well aligned, so that run-off, with consequent formation of gullies, will not arise at times of heavy rainfall. The master plan is the working guide for layout demarcation, but as field operations proceed, farmers and foresters should be prepared to effect changes of detail here and there if closer examination of the land shows that there is justification for them. This discrepancy between the ideal layout drawn upon the map and the facts discovered by clearance of the actual ground calls for the exercise of ingenuity and flexibility. No two areas are exactly alike and so plans differ in minor particulars according to the needs and circumstances of projects.

Forest-farm layouts should always allow for speedy and convenient access to all sections of the plantations. If possible, existing tracks suitable for conversion into roads can be extended or realigned. Any livestock kept should as far as practicable be driven along open or grazing strips, since in large numbers they will soon damage dirt highways. Nurseries require siting near water points, which may be wells, boreholes, rivers and streams or other sources of supply. The arboreta should be placed conveniently to facilitate transfer of plants intended for special testing or seed-multiplication work. Windbreaks perform important tasks, and can be planted as additions to the general crop production blocks. Any exposed places will benefit from the establishment of staggered rows of trees as an outer shield. Another method is to tilt sections on flat land so that the prevailing wind does not strike their leading sides or edges directly, or else arrange them in alternate or bricklayer's pattern with grazing strips facing towards unbroken lines of trees. In areas where very narrow pasture and

Fig 6. Tilted pattern of forest-farm blocks

Note alternate halves of every third block remain under grass or herbage

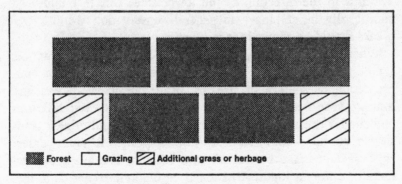

Fig 7. Alternate pattern of forest-farm blocks

The open strips face unbroken lines of trees

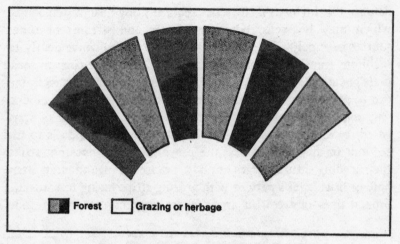

Fig 8. Fan pattern of forest-farm blocks

herbage belts must be used initially, a larger extent of grassland may be obtained by leaving the alternate half of every third block unplanted. Plantations can be laid out on fan patterns when the configuration of the land requires a circular layout. In this case blocks take on the approximate shape of blunt-ended wedges. As an aid in conserving moisture on steep hillsides, a trench type of water flow check or series of *banquettes* is excellent. Here, both the upper and lower boundaries of each contour belt of forest are lined by a shallow ditch, the bottom of which inclines upwards in the direction of the lower side. This technique can additionally be employed in general conservation works. Firebreaks should be allowed for in layouts.

Whenever applicable, normal land-improvement practices should be introduced. These cover such items as check dams, protection of sources of streams, proper drainage in wet and marshy localities, maintenance of cover on exposed hill tops and similar measures. Renovation of degraded and eroded lands should go hand in hand with tree planting. In sandy desert regions, dunes may be treated with oil sludge sprays and stabilisers of different kinds. All cleared vegetation, except large tree trunks which can be carried away for fuel, should be cut up and left to rot away on the sites. In time, such material will perform a useful purpose in increasing the quantity of humus present in the soil. Drainage, natural or artificial, is essential, the object being to encourage the absorption of rain water and its collection below the surface of the land, as well as to keep the soil fairly porous, discourage the retention of stagnant pools and ensure good distribution of available moisture. On steep lands, open or contour drains are very effective. Terraces, low hedges and banks protected by cover crops of perennial type are other useful ways of improving the fertility of hilly ground. In dry zones, irrigation is frequently installed to improve plant growth and yields and the siting of suitable channels with well positioned outlets calls for skilful field layouts.

FOREST NURSERIES AND ARBORETA

Tree nurseries are really a combination of plant maternity homes and seedling crèches. Within the forest nursery, the important tasks of seed sowing, germination, propagation, transplanting, budding and grafting, and growing on take place. Because it is important to ensure that plants get good starts in life, the organisation and layout of their early surroundings are matters of some consequence. The actual size of any nursery depends upon the extent of the area that it has to serve and the output that will be demanded from it. Proper siting of nurseries assists efficient operation and eliminates wasteful delays on the production line.

It is best to find sites for forest nurseries within the areas selected for initial development. This obviates the transport of young trees over long distances and minimises losses from consequent exposure. A permanent water supply is essential, as well as shelter from wind, light shade, and easy access. Places like sheltered hollows, provided that they are not too damp or susceptible to being flooded, with streams running through them, are good sites. Do not, however, choose positions that may be classed as frost 'pockets' or which suffer excessively from cold-air drainage in cool areas.

Arboreta are tree gardens or miniature plantations, in which selected specimens of different species of trees and shrubs may be grown for trial, or else for multiplication purposes. Normally,

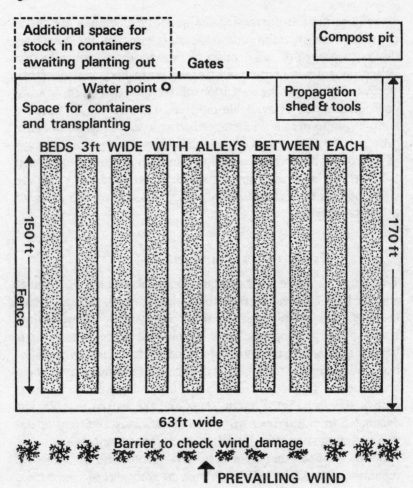

Additional space for stock in containers awaiting planting out

Gates

Compost pit

Water point O
Space for containers and transplanting

Propagation shed & tools

BEDS 3ft WIDE WITH ALLEYS BETWEEN EACH

150 ft

Fence

170 ft

63 ft wide

Barrier to check wind damage

↑ PREVAILING WIND

Fig 9. Typical layout for a tree nursery

each arboretum will contain a number of different types of plants, chosen for their vigour and fine qualities. From these specimens, forest farmers can collect seed or grafting material to use in the main plantations. Every nursery should have arboreta located within the area it serves, of from one to five acres in area. The conditions in arboreta should reproduce on a small and condensed scale those that are likely to be encountered in the big forest blocks and belts, as far as may be practicable. Different sites should be used for testing. In this way, it becomes possible to evaluate the responses of newly introduced species and also to create a reserve of high-quality planting material for extension work. Young trees can be transferred easily from the forest nurseries to the arboreta and placed under daily observation there.

PLANTATIONS

Special attention is given in forest farming to the need for effective soil and water conservation. Hence the importance of proper alignment of forest belts. If the task of siting them is not correctly done, the whole scheme may fail. By following the land contours carefully and observing proper vertical intervals between successive plantings, an easily worked farm can be built up progressively. On flat or gently sloping localities, belts normally give way to blocks, which should be designed to conform to the shape of the area in question. Widths of more than 300 yards are normally difficult to cope with at harvest time and there is also greater risk of fire spreading in dry regions if the distances are excessive.

Young plantations should be protected by moveable fencing from damage by livestock. Another point to remember is to guard against the risk of fire by incorporating firebreaks at appropriate intervals in belts. The width of any grazing or open strips is adequate to prevent fire spreading across them at most times, but there could be a possibility of flames running down the length of a belt or block of trees or through dry grass. The breaks also provide passageways for vehicles and give access at times of harvesting. In cases of doubt, it is worthwhile to make allowance for including strips of bare ground, some twenty yards in width, along the sides of plantations and pasture or herbage sections. If there is any danger of erosion, small banks must be constructed to prevent run-off after heavy storms.

EXPANSION

The first plantings are always the most difficult but once exotic species and methods have been introduced and taken hold in unfamiliar regions, it is far simpler to expand. The basis having been laid, the next moves are easier. All biological material is subject to change and progress or retardation. It cannot remain static. So forest farming will either succeed or fail very much according to the planning of its component parts. Assessments of expansion potential should take into account the estimated growth rates of tree species, the capacity of the labour to clear and mark out contour belts and blocks and the ability of the nurseries to produce the necessary planting material. In addition, other questions such as the scope for the sale of produce and the arrangements for marketing require proper consideration. Pilot schemes in new regions will test the responses of the introduced species to the local circumstances and show which types of tree crops may thrive and yield profits. But when it comes to subsequent large-scale expansion it is vital that any general schemes of layout should make provision from the beginning for progressive expansion as an integral part of the whole project.

FORM OF SURVEY FOR THE COLLECTION OF INFORMATION ABOUT A
LOCALITY AND ITS USEFULNESS FOR THE GROWING OF TREE CROPS

PROJECT:

PART I — ECOLOGY

(a) *Site:*

(b) *Natural vegetation:*

	Trees	Shrubs	Grasses	Other types	Barren
Species & genus					

Present vegetation :
(if changed by developments)
Life forms :
(Note if drought-resistant, conventional, or other types.)

(c) *Habitat factors:*

    (i) *Climatic:*

        Rainfall (monthly average in inches)
                Jan. Feb. Mar. Apr. May Jun. Jul. Aug. Sep. Oct. Nov. Dec.
        Humidity
        Saturation deficit
        Wind (prevailing and intensity)

Temperature (monthly average in °F or °C)
Maximum
Minimum
> Jan. Feb. Mar. Apr. May Jun. Jul. Aug. Sept. Oct. Nov. Dec.

Light (average hours)
> Jan. Feb. Mar. Apr. May Jun. Jul. Aug. Sep. Oct. Nov. Dec.

Other influences

(ii) *Physiographic:*

Elevation (above sea level)
Slope
Erosion
Denudation
Cold-air drainage
Waterlogging
Salinity
Other influences

(iii) *Edaphic:*

Soil type

Soil mineral matter	Coarse sand	Fine sand	Silt	Clay	Other
Mechanical composition					

Organic matter
Humus and organisms
Solution acidity (pH)

Soil water	Hygroscopic (unavailable)	Capillary (available)	Gravitational (water table)	pF

Soil atmosphere
  and drainage
Soil temperatures
Other influences

(iv) *Biotic:*

Human activities
Animals (grazing, trampling, etc.)
Plants (preferences, light and shade or microclimate, competition, spread and other relevant matters)
Pests and diseases already in evidence

(d) *General:*

(Enter any further comments including likely effects, adverse or favourable, of developments upon the local and adjacent habitats.)

PART II — ECONOMICS

(a) *Economic Factors:*
(Mention markets and costs)

(b) *Situation:*
(Transport facilities, and other important details)

PART III — SILVICULTURE/PASTURAGE/LIVESTOCK

(a) *Cultural facilities afforded:* (State briefly the conditions offered to crops as deduced from Part I.)
Trees and shrubs :
Grasses and herbage :
Livestock (types) :

(b) *Special requirements:*
Protection :
Environmental limits :
(Heat, cold, aridity,
salinity, etc.)
Conservation :
Controls :
Buildings and equipment :
Other needs :

Any further factors:

7
Planting and Cropping

THERE ARE three principles which are fundamental to the success of a forest farm. These are:

1, the species chosen should fit in satisfactorily with the local habitat, allowing for progressive development designed to ameliorate unfavourable conditions;
2, the whole unit or series of units must be capable of achieving a harmonious and balanced output;
3, there must be an economic basis of proved utilitarian value that will produce profits.

The growth of trees and other plants is influenced by soils, climate, latitude, altitude, the form and slope of land surfaces, distance from the sea, the presence of ponds, lakes, rivers, streams and underground aquifers, local weather patterns and average rainfall.

Over long periods species have adapted themselves to differing conditions, so that the characteristics of, for example, phanerophytes or therophytes bear little resemblance to those of xerophytes, succulents, or hydrophytes. Seasonal variations exercise marked effects upon flowering and fruiting. In some colder regions the winter is extended and harsh, so plants undergo periods of dormancy. On the other hand, at certain locations in the tropics there is no definitive boundary between seasons. Subtropical areas normally have a dry or cool time of the year and there are usually major and minor rainy months. Quite frequently, aberrations occur in the distribution of a year's weather, causing failures of crops and related hardships.

Another significant influence is that of aspect. Particularly in hilly areas, where there are high ridges alternating with valleys, places quite close to each other may have very distinctive conditions. Even within the lower lying lands, one section of a valley can possess cool and damp characteristics, due to partial shade, whilst the opposite parts may be dry and warm, being exposed to greater direct sunshine. Strong winds cause excessive evaporation and damage to plants, as well as loss of good soil from erosion. The nature of the land, too, exercises profound effects upon climate. Sandy ground radiates more heat than does clay, so that districts with light soils normally have higher daytime temperatures. At night, however, the fall in temperature is less in regions of heavy land than it is in deserts. The beneficial influences of irrigation in arid countries are well known, not only in the immediate vicinity of the canals and dams but also over adjacent localities.

Land for tree crops may not need to be stumped or cleared completely of any existing vegetation. Useless bush should be cut down to ankle height. If there is no native tree cover, or simply a sparse or negligible covering of grass and other plants, so much the better. The lines of the forest blocks or belts should be marked out with short white painted posts, normally placed at fifty-yard intervals, or perhaps closer on very broken ground. According to the species of trees to be utilized, different numbers of planting holes must be dug, with a shallow basin formed from the excavated soil around each one. Leave these holes open for up to a week or two before transplanting begins. This allows the earth to settle and avoids later caving in of ground around the young trees. Usually, holes some two feet in depth and up to two and a half feet across will be satisfactory, but much depends upon the types of trees to be planted. An acre can contain from about twenty to two hundred plants, according to their size and growth potential. It is therefore necessary to be sure of the crop's requirements before deciding on the distances between planting holes and the number that must be dug to the acre. The most suitable arrangement is the quincunx pattern, a method of alternate planting. Do not waste any part of forest blocks or belts and try to ensure that the edges present a solid and unbroken front outwards. The planting of contour belts often demands some ingenuity in arranging good distribution of trees and the utilisation of all available space, owing to the changing lines of direction.

Any grazing and herbage strips need to be only about one third of the average width of forest belts and blocks. On these, the land should be cleared to ground level and treated, if necessary, with arboricides and herbicides as quickly as possible. Controlled firing of strips is often practised and can be most effective in dry weather, if due care is taken. Unless irrigation is available in plantations, sowing of seed *in situ* will normally be confined to the beginning of the wet season in arid regions, or in temperate zones at the conventional times employed in local forestry or farming programmes. The removal of obectionable tree cover in certain areas often results in the increased growth of native grass species, which have been known to double or treble their yields in a single season. Machinery is available for tree planting and where climatic conditions permit some species can be set out using tractor drawn planting boards in deep drills.

PROPAGATION

The necessity of using only the best quality material in forest farming cannot be stressed too much. This dictum covers both the question of the strain or variety of any species (or in more advanced terms the hybrid or cultivar) and the vigour and appearance. Imperfectly formed planting material should never be employed for propagation purposes. In selecting seeds, care must be taken to choose those produced by healthy stock. Perfect seed normally comes from plants which have been well cultivated and looked after and have received adequate nourishment. Again, unless seeds are fully ripe before gathering, their germinative ability and the vitality of the seedlings can be affected seriously. In the case of some species carefully stored seeds may retain their vitality for several years, but as a general rule old seeds are less useful than fresh ones and in addition the plants produced from them are frequently weak and slow growing. Seeds vary much in size and type according to the species concerned, but generally they do best in fine, well pulverised soil, if possible of lighter kind, to which has been added some compost. The surfaces of beds for seed sowing should be level, with stones and rubbish removed. If there is any likelihood of insect eggs or larvae being present in the earth, boiling water or chemical treatment should be given.

Similarly, in damp areas it is worthwhile to apply fungicides as a precautionary measure. As a general rule seeds should be covered with enough soil to equal the width at their shortest diameters, though there are many exceptions to this. Larger or slower germinating ones need sowing at greater depths than do quick developing types, while those in pots or boxes or planting baskets and containers require less covering than others sown in beds. Row sowing should always be practised whenever possible, because it simplifies nursery work. It is far easier to water and weed plants in rows than to attend to haphazard and scattered seedlings. Sometimes large seeds may be affected in germination by the manner of placement in the soil, causing deformity. Generally, the micropyle should point downwards, but some seeds like coconuts should be laid on their sides.

Where immense numbers of young plants must be produced or where other difficulties of production arise, it is easiest to sow seeds in forest nursery beds, subsequently moving them with balls of soil around their roots to field positions. However, better results with less losses may be secured by either transplanting the seedlings from the beds into baskets or various types of containers in the nursery, or sowing direct into the containers, subsequently transferring the partially established trees without any disturbance straight out to their final sites. Sowing at stake, or *in situ*, in the belts or blocks may be practicable in some localities, but it can result in greater mortality of valuable plants and should only be employed where large or surplus quantities of seed are available. If seeds are very small they can be mixed before sowing with a filler of fine sand or sawdust, which facilitates even distribution in the beds. Overcrowding of seedlings should be avoided, since it often leads to losses from fungoid disease or malformation of the young plants. Containers for nursery work can be made from polythene sheeting, grass or rushes, large leaves sewn together, or bamboos. Large tins, with holes punched in the bottoms, are also quite useful. Grass baskets are easy to make, simply requiring two bundles of fairly dry, but not brittle, material. These are laid at right angles to one another, then bent up to form the sides leaving a stretch of grass at the base to form the bottom of the basket. The tops are plaited and two strips of tree fibre tied at intervals

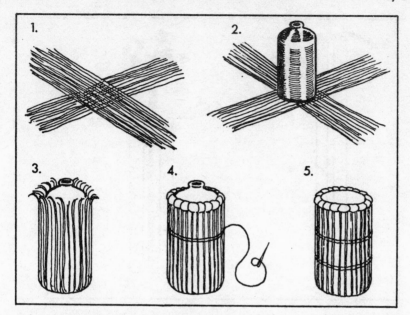

Fig 10. Making grass baskets for tree seedlings

1. Lay bundles of dry grass at right angles
2. Place a bottle or jar in the middle
3. Bend up the grass. It may be dampened to facilitate the operation
4. Plait the top and bind the side with fibre
5. Remove the container to leave the basket

around the circumference of the container to hold it firm. Bamboo pots are sections of the stems with one node left intact, except for a drainage hole. At planting out time, they must be split down each side and pulled slightly apart to permit egress for the roots into the surrounding ground. For species with long delicate taproots, such as carobs, it is a good plan to prepare containers consisting of four thin laths or lengths of wood filled with earth, and held together by encircling bonds of twine or wire. These can be up to three or more feet long, and provide ample room for the development of the rooting system, also allowing speedy and efficient planting out when the time comes.

To secure good germination, with rapid initial growth, there should be enough moisture, adequate warmth, fresh air, and some protection from strong and scorching sunlight. If the seed coat or

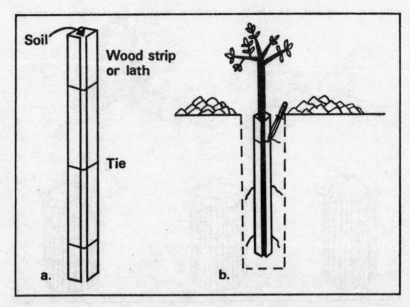

Fig 11. Planting container for trees with long delicate taproots, such as carobs

a. Four strips of wood are tied together with wire or string
b. Plant the container with the young tree in it. The ties are cut to permit the developing roots to emerge

testa is very hard, it will be necessary to treat the seeds by pouring boiling water over them and leaving them to soak for about twenty-four hours before sowing. This softens the testa and aids quick development. Sometimes the period of soaking may be lengthened. Species like algarobas, carobs, and others need this treatment. Alternatively, rasping of the testas may be practised, using files or grindstones; or else steeping in a weak solution of formic acid (1/500); soaking in water to which two drops of chlorine have been added to every fluid ounce (2.84 cl), or in a weak solution of ammonia or water and camphor. It is desirable to carry out germination tests on batches of seed, to ascertain what percentage is viable, before spending time on sowing them in nurseries. This may be done on damp blotting paper or thick cloth. Soaking beforehand in hot water can often increase the number germinating.

In forest nurseries the ground should be cleared of vegetation, all debris being removed, and then well dug over and, where practicable, levelled off. The beds may be made of any convenient size, but a satisfactory width is three feet with any desired length. This enables the attendants to care for the young plants without having to tread on the seedbed itself. In between each bed there should be a walk or alley wide enough to permit a wheelbarrow or trolley to pass along; usually three to four feet is adequate for the purpose. The earth in the beds should be well dug over to a depth of at least a foot and the subsoil broken up by a crowbar below. In wet places it is advantageous to raise the level of beds a few inches above the surrounding ground, but in dry localities where rainfall is limited, slightly sunken or normal ones are in order. High beds can, however, be damaged by heavy precipitation, thus exposing or washing away the seeds, so they should always have a low retaining wall around them, about three inches in height. This can be made from planks, metal strips, mud plaster, or even flat stones.

The surface soil of the nursery beds must be brought to a fine tilth by hoeing and raking and any stones removed. Do not apply fresh manure; use only dry dung, compost, or leaf mould, well sifted. Heavy soils, such as clay, can be improved by the incorporation of sand or wood ashes, while light ground will benefit from the addition of plenty of organic matter. It is simple in most areas to make compost in pits, using vegetable refuse. See that it heats up properly or else weeds may become a problem, due to the presence of viable seeds in the mixture. If compost or dry manures are unobtainable, recourse may have to be made to light applications of fertilisers if the soil is seriously deficient in essential nutrients, to begin with, but later on the leaves of newly planted trees can be turned into good humus for nursery beds. Shading in hot areas is necessary. The shades can be made from grass mats, rushes, roofing felt, or any other available materials, fixed on short posts, about three feet above the surfaces of the beds. These will admit morning and evening sunshine, but exclude noontime scorch. Shelter from wind can be provided by using screens and other breaks.

Forest nurseries should have one corner set aside for the erection of a propagating shed. Here will also be kept such items as tools, budding and grafting equipment, labels and cans. In very arid localities, instead of sheds, pits may be employed. A pit is normally some three to four feet deep, with a roof of light poles or sticks covered with leaves or matting. At the bottom, a layer of sand, suitably moistened, will assist the maintenance of a more humid atmosphere in which cuttings may be rooted quickly, hard shelled seeds induced to germinate, and backward plants encouraged to form new growth. In cold regions, glasshouses can be valuable for work of this kind. Supplies of planting containers, materials for making transplanting baskets and similar receptacles should be stored in a shed until required for use. The actual size of forest nurseries will naturally depend upon the extent of the area to be served, and the output expected from them, as well as the species to be cultured. Nurseries of about one quarter to one half of an acre are quite manageable, but there are no fixed rules and the matter is one of individual choice. However, room should always be left for expansion near by.

Many species propagate easily from cuttings and in doubtful cases a rooting hormone should be employed. Suitable cuttings should be taken from firm and properly mature shoots and set in a good rooting medium made up of light soil or sand, kept moderately damp. The growing medium must be pressed down gently around them, with the cutting in a slightly slanting position. Shelter and appropriate warmth combined with adequate ventilation are necessary and good results are more likely to be secured in propagating pits, nursery sheds, or greenhouses and frames than out in the open. The ground end of the shoot should be cut across cleanly at an angle of some forty-five degrees, and if there are many large upper leaves these should be pinched off, leaving only a minimum of foliage on the cutting. Tree cuttings should be slit or split a little at the bottoms before being inserted in the rooting place. The best time for taking cuttings is at the beginning of the active growth season. In many cases, the upper shoots of crop-bearing trees will yield more productive planting material than the lower parts. Always see that cuttings have about three to four eyes or buds underneath the medium when setting them. The point of severance from the parent stock must be through or just below a node or leaf bud. Striking cuttings is not very difficult if the conditions are suitable and special care is given to the more obstinate ones. Rooting hormones are most efficacious, while bell jars, bottles filled with water, and plastic covers or special shades can help in many instances.

Layering, marcottage, ring barking, as well as propagation by means of suckers, buds, roots, root division, and rhizomes are other common methods of increasing stock, and full details of these techniques will be found in books on arboriculture and horticulture or orchard work. Whether or not layering is employed to any great extent will depend upon the time and labour available, but it can be most useful for multiplying superior stock in arboreta. Marcottage is helpful in cases of difficult species, where ordinary cuttings do not normally succeed. Crops like breadnuts are usually increased by detaching suckers from the stems, and to obtain a heavy output of these gourmandisers, as they are termed, the trees should be well pruned or pollarded to encourage them to produce suckers freely. Algarobas propagate readily from root cuttings or division of young plants. The employment of rhizomes is generally confined to grasses and smaller species.

It is important to remember that the taking of cuttings, or the multiplication of planting stock by similar means, is vegetative or asexual propagation, as distinct from reproduction by seed, which is sexual. The plants resulting from cuttings are clones or types of carefully selected parent stock with standardised characteristics. Clones cannot be further improved, except by optimum cultural conditions to a very slight extent. Sexually propagated plants can however vary considerably in their qualities, though open to betterment by programmes of cross breeding and hybridisation. Unless a variety or cultivar is known to reproduce true to type, it is always advantageous to use cuttings whenever practicable. For rootstocks, on the other hand, strong and vigorous seedlings are essential to get the best results.

Grafting and budding are important in forest nursery work, and these two practices are particularly valuable in the cultivation of species like carobs, walnuts, and persimmons. Through grafting it becomes possible to multiply on a large scale the good qualities of selected varieties, induce earlier bearing, and bring together the two sexes of dioecious trees on one stock, so ensuring consistent pollination of flowers. In all grafting and budding work it is vital to select stock carefully. Both stock and scion should have similar natural vigour and affinity. The actual operation is best carried out in shade, the grafted or budded parts being protected by wax or plastic strips until the union is complete. There must be direct contact between the cambium tissues of both scion and rootstock, otherwise union will not occur. Though grafting and budding may be done after planting out, it is normally easier to undertake the task while the plants are still in the nursery, where they can be checked more speedily and any failures replaced.

According to the sizes and types of the subjects, different methods of grafting can be employed. Whip or tongue grafts are popular in cooler areas, while saddle grafting is most suitable for shrubs and young plants. For larger trees, crown or rind techniques are excellent. In side grafting, scions are inserted under the bark of the stock. Inarching or grafting by approach is common in the tropics, the pots or containers of stocks being placed under the specimen which is to furnish scions. When the parts have united, the scions are cut off individually from the parent tree.

Budding is simply a form of grafting in which the bud with a small portion of bark attached to it is fitted into a cut of corresponding dimensions in the stem or branch of another plant. Before removing buds it is important to see that the sap is circulating actively in the subject of operation, otherwise it may be impossible to detach the bark satisfactorily. There are several kinds of budding, including the techniques of shield or T budding, flute or tube, ring or annular, and graft or patch budding. Shield budding is the most common for fruit bearing species. Here, the well developed but dormant buds are extracted by inserting a sharp pointed knife some half an inch below the bud in question between the wood and the inner bark, then sloping it outwards to lift out a small piece of wood as well. In the bark of the young tree in which the bud is to be placed an incision is now made in the form of a T, the bark raised carefully and the bud pushed gently into the opened section. The cut is then bound securely with wax and tape or plastic strips to exclude air. Only the tip of the bud is left exposed. The job of budding must be done quickly and skilfully, the best times being early morning or evening, when there is no strong sun overhead. Patch budding is similar, but instead of sliding the bud under the bark, a rectangular piece of the latter is cut away and the scion fitted into the space left.

Special budding knives are available, as well as grafting wax, polythene plastic strips for budding and tying, and raffia or tape, if preferred. Grafting or budding wax is made by mixing four parts by weight of powdered natural resin, two parts of beeswax, and one part of tallow. These are first melted in a pan and then stirred thoroughly. Softened paraffin wax can be used in emergencies.

The internal arrangements of propagation grounds or nurseries should allow for smooth progression from seed sowing or rooting of cuttings to transplanting into containers for eventual planting out and tasks like grafting and budding. Proper organisation aids efficient and speedy multiplication of plants, so that the production line functions with the minimum of effort and confusion. Scrupulous hygiene and strict phyto-sanitary precautions must be observed. Smoking and deposition of rubbish should never be permitted in forest nurseries. To check the spread of disease, the attendants' hands should be washed regularly and clothing of suitable standards and condition worn. Transplanting should be carried out at a steady momentum, so that losses are reduced to a minimum. Apart from the necessary facilities such as sheds, propagating pits or shelters and tool and seed stores, the nursery should possess a good compost-making section and supplies of extra soil for replenishing and remaking seed beds, as the young plants are moved out and new lots started. By ensuring that everything is arranged conveniently, there will be no hold-ups in growth and output. Because nurseries are key factors in the efficient working of forest farms, a little extra thought and care spent on them will be well repaid.

PLANTING

The transference of young plants from the nursery to forest blocks and belts on open ground may be compared in some ways to the weaning of a child or the despatch to boarding school of boys and girls who have hitherto known only the sheltered conditions of home life. Plants suffer from shock just as people do, only the effects are entirely physical. Hence the importance of mitigating the setbacks that planting out can give rise to if the work is not carefully done. As far as possible, removal from nursery to plantation should be undertaken at the start of a wet season, especially if the young trees have not already been established in containers. If irrigation of some form is available, the grower will have a greater choice of times. The best period of the day to plant out is late in the afternoon in warmer regions, though this does not matter very much in temperate or cold localities. Unless heavy rain may be expected, a good watering should follow at once in dry areas. In this connexion, it is worth pointing out that one adequate watering is better than a dozen sprinklings, which fail to penetrate the root zone and soon evaporate from the surface. Great care should be taken not to injure or bend improperly the young roots, but to give these ample room in the planting holes. Trees and shrubs should always be set out in rows, to facilitate harvesting or under-planting, and for forest farms the quincunx pattern is favoured generally.

To obtain correct spacing, the areas should be lined beforehand, that is pegs should be driven into the ground at the appropriate intervals to mark the places where the holes are to be dug. Make sure that the holes all lie on the same sides of the pegs in any given block or section of a belt so that the direction remains constant.

Holes of too small a size will cause stunted growth of plants. This is particularly noticeable in poorer land. While hole size will depend upon the type of material and the kind of soil, the average dimensions of holes are usually two feet deep and two and a half feet in diameter for most species, assuming a height of not over three feet at planting-out time. (For species such as *Ceratonia siliqua*, a greater depth will be necessary to accommodate the long taproots.) The bottoms of the cavities can be broken up by a crowbar where the subsoil is hard or compressed. Filling in must be done with care, the plants being left erect and the earth firmed around them. In hot, dry regions, the soil can be slightly lower in the planting holes than the level of the surrounding ground, but in very wet or cold places it is preferable to raise up the height to

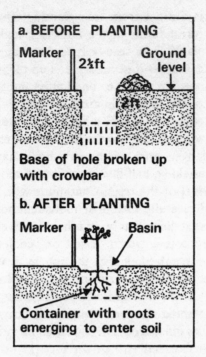

a. BEFORE PLANTING

Marker   2½ft   Ground level

Base of hole broken up with crowbar

b. AFTER PLANTING

Marker   Basin

Container with roots emerging to enter soil

Fig 12. Planting holes

Planting out trees for cropping. A hole is excavated and the base broken up. After planting is completed, a basin is left to hold moisture

a few inches above that of the adjacent land. After a week or two, a check should be made to see that no cracks have appeared in the filled-in holes and the trees are firm and straight. Any open parts should be attended to without delay. The object of leaving a depression or basin at the top of the planting hole after filling in, is to conserve moisture and make subsequent mulching easy. Conversely, a slightly raised level of soil discourages the accumulation of stagnant water around young plants. In course of time, weathering will reduce the small mounds or add to the lower levels, making them indistinguishable from neighbouring parts of the plantation. As a general rule, planting can be shallower in damp and cold localities than it will be in warm and dry regions. It is frequently done by machinery, especially with conifers, in standard forest practice.

Planting out is distinct from transplanting. The latter usually takes place on forest farms in the nurseries, and consists of removing young plants from seed-beds to containers. When established, budded or grafted if necessary and up to two to three feet in height, the trees are ready to be planted out in the arboreta, blocks, or belts of the main field areas. In cases where containers are not employed, a ball of soil may be kept around the plant's roots during moving. Puddling with thick viscid mud is also quite effective. The planting hole, when used, should have been dug beforehand, and should be half-filled with water about an hour previous to the arrival of the trees. Containers with plants in them may be dropped carefully into their individual holes and the soil filled in and pressed down firmly. In other instances, where young trees have their roots enclosed in soil or puddled, even gentler handling will be required. Finish the job by watering liberally and, if available, scatter a covering of dry or wilted vegetation as a mulch on top of the filled-in hole. In arid areas, the basins left around newly planted out trees will catch any rainfall. Sometimes, small shades made from twigs, plaited palm fronds, or other material, can be fixed on two or three sticks over the recently moved plants. Any subsequent field waterings will depend upon the season of the year, the incidence of natural precipitation and the progress of the stands. If damage is possible from farm animals or wild game, tree guards or protective barriers should be erected immediately. (See also p. 152.)

It is most important that each planting-out operation should be prepared for in advance. The holes should be dug beforehand, the water added to each one, and all arrangements made to ensure rapid and speedy completion of the work. Delays mean eventual loss of plants. The trees to be moved should be assembled in a convenient part of the nursery the day previous to that chosen for the operation, so that they can be transported quickly to the sites in the plantations. Efficient organisation is therefore vital.

The correct distances for planting of different species vary according to the types in question and the local conditions. Trees may attain larger sizes on good land than they do in poor or marginal areas. On light soils, a general guideline is to space out plants at distances approximately equal to their allowable height, while on better ground one can add about a third to this. Nevertheless, in controlled forest farming, it is inadvisable to permit trees to grow too tall, otherwise harvesting becomes more difficult. If trimming is practised therefore, planting distances as a normal rule will conform to the principle that spacing should keep in pace with optimum allowable height, each case being decided on its merits. The table given here shows how many plants will be required to set out per acre at distances of from one to fifty feet apart. To find out any numbers not included, divide 43560 (the number of square feet in one acre) by the square of the distance apart you want the trees to be in feet. The result is the number of plants needed per acre.

PLANTING DISTANCES

Distance apart (feet)	Number of plants to the acre	Distance apart (feet)	Number of plants to the acre
1	43560	15	193
1½	19360	16	170
2	10890	17	150
2½	6970	18	134
3	4840	19	120
3½	3556	20	108
4	2722	22	90
5	1742	24	75
6	1210	26	64
7	1037	28	55
8	889	30	48
9	680	32	42
10	537	35	35
11	435	37	32
12	302	40	27
13	257	45	21
14	222	50	18

Assuming a controlled height of forest-farm plantations of from twenty to thirty feet, or occasionally a little more, the number of trees to the acre averages from 108 to 48. If regular pruning is practised, it is seldom necessary to plant trees at distances over thirty feet and to do so would reduce yields. Normally, about twenty to twenty-five feet is ideal, though smaller forms

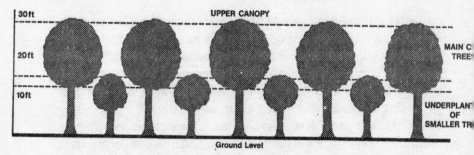

Fig 13. Layering or method of planting mixed species

A bottom layer of shorter trees or shrubs may often be planted under blocks or belts of taller species where the upper canopy is open enough to admit sufficient light

may be as close as ten to fifteen feet in plantations. The importance of using only high-yielding, selected, good quality cultivars and strains must be emphasised if superior results are required.

Planting is normally slightly closer than it is in, say, horticultural work, which gives greater density. For smaller species or shrubs, from 1,000 to 150 per acre is common practice, while in nurseries, plants for budding and grafting or growing on can be spaced as little as one foot apart.

CULTURAL OPERATIONS

Often sites for field plantings may be prepared by cutting down indigenous vegetation, if any, to ankle level, thereafter controlling its regeneration by occasional slashing or the application of selective herbicides, arboricides, and weedkillers. Once the newly introduced trees grow tall and form a canopy, with perhaps a secondary ground layer of economic shrubs, they should suppress effectively any undesired native species. On grazing strips, it is necessary to eliminate useless scrub and worthless trees down to ground level, sometimes spraying the areas to kill off weed growth and if necessary reseeding with grass or herbage capable of thriving under the local conditions. Both soil- and foliage-applied chemicals may be employed for the task, if desired, and there is a wide choice available to operators. Selective weedkillers can also be useful. Where such treatments are not desired or possible, periodic cutting down of objectionable plants becomes necessary. In some places, stands of valuable native species may be found and these should be preserved, after thinning and proper attention, the most superior specimens being utilised for seed collection and propagation.

Trees in belts or blocks require normal forest care and cultural treatment, including sometimes trimming and removal of diseased or dead branches, or parts damaged in storms. The natural fall of leaves every season will provide the soil in plantations with vegetable manure and increase its humus content. In addition, decomposed foliage helps the land to retain moisture, discourages erosion or run off, checks radiation, suppresses weeds and improves general conditions for plant life. Before trees attain full maturity there will be several years during which forest farmers can raise catch crops between rows of young specimens. Such subsidiary or inter crops yield immediate profits and bridge in part the gap or interval that must elapse before forests begin to bear. Moreover, they control regeneration of weed growth, so making upkeep simpler and often assist in guarding against high incidence of pests. The surface cover or mulch provided is very beneficial. Apart from green manuring types, herbaceous perennials, especially any belonging to the Leguminosae family, which fix atmospheric nitrogen in the soil in many cases, are very valuable. Cash crops, such as cassava, vegetables, tobacco, groundnuts, cotton, as well as essential oil-yielding species, fodder plants, species for drugs and medicinal use and many others are good choices. It is, of course, desirable to select kinds that require the minimum of cultivation.

The suppression of scrub bushes and worthless trees on most land generally results in a marked increase in grass ground cover. Provided objectionable plants are eliminated, this should be encouraged. To supplement the native species, a wide range of exotic pasture or forage grasses and herbage types may be introduced, according to the circumstances prevailing in the areas in question. Sowing should only be attempted at the start of wet periods, the land being raked or harrowed and then seeded at the average rates of from fifteen to twenty pounds per acre. To aid germination and establishment, the decomposing foliage of the previous vegetative cover should be spread over the seed that has been scattered on the land, or in desert and barren places blends of synthetic rubber and oil or latex based emulsions may be sprayed over the surface to form protective skins until the young grass plants have rooted. Any pasture and grazing strips should be supplied with ample and well distributed lots of animal manure by the passage of the herds of livestock along them at regular intervals.

Minimal pruning gives better control of trees and enables growers to compel plants to assume forms that will facilitate harvesting and add to productivity. Pruning and heading should start when trees and shrubs are young. The aim is to create evenly balanced heads, with regular radiation of branches outwards from the centre. Upright shoots possess greater vitality. The exact mode of trimming varies in different areas, but generally speaking the following points should be borne in mind, remembering that no elaborate work, as required in orthodox fruit orchards, or in tree-surgery, is necessary for general purposes.

(a) Try to keep trees to moderate heights, with clean crowns and well spaced branches.

(b) Allow good circulation of air and light.

(c) If compelled to trim a badly balanced mature specimen, use a sharp saw and cut in a slanting or upright direction, so that any ends will throw off rain, and leave smooth surfaces.

(d) In such cases, do not leave stumps on trunk or branches. Instead cut close to the outside of the part from which you are removing the useless portion.

(e) Cover bad wounds with coal tar or suitable emulsion.

(f) Do not trim during drought, or when trees are bearing or starting growth of new buds and leaves.

(g) As minimal pruning is designed to enable better harvesting and higher yields to be obtained, remember to adjust the operation to the needs of both the trees and the forest farm.

Whenever possible, trees should be encouraged to form low

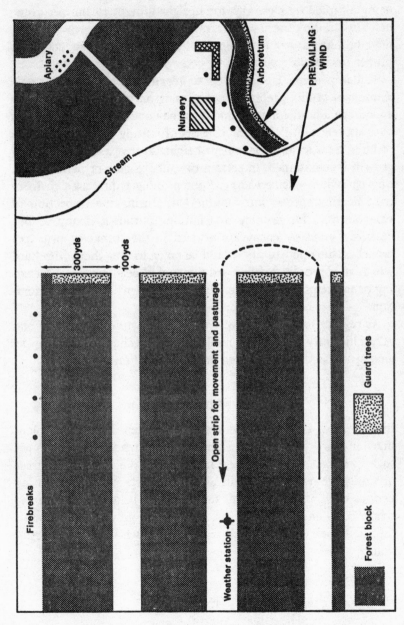

Fig 14. Example of placement of guard trees to provide protection from the prevailing wind in harsh climatic conditions

spreading forms with maximum bearing areas, the new shoots being afforded ample room for upright growth to the permitted heights. On the other hand, certain sections of tree growing units may be left to attain maximum heights for the production of timber for building purposes, or poles and posts for fencing.

Collar pruning is employed to regenerate old shrubs, while thumbnail pruning refers to the nipping off of terminal shoots to encourage a branching top and must be done when plants are not over six feet tall. Pollarding consists of cutting off the main stem of large trees to any convenient height, so that a desired limit of growth is maintained. In certain cases, coppicing or periodic cutting back also aids spreading. Root pruning is practised to force fruit bearing species into production. During the inspection of valuable trees for pruning or trimming purposes, if any serious cavities caused by decay are noticed in the trunks or principal branches, the opportunity should be taken to plug them with hard wood, after proper cleaning and removal of dead material. A coating of tar helps preserve the filling and prevent further deterioration.

As regards harvesting, tree crops can be gathered speedily and very efficiently by suction methods and mechanical shaking devices, such as those employed in commercial olive groves.

GUARD TREES

In cold areas or exposed localities it is often desirable to plant lines of guard trees around stands of more tender species. Types such as Sitka spruce, Japanese larch, hardy pines and other trees of similar characteristics will give protection and shelter during periods of winter weather to the blocks or belts of crop bearing species very effectively. This is, of course, simply an extension of the shelterbelt or windbreak technique, much used in afforestation.

Useful species include : —

> *Acacia dealbata*, Silver Wattle.
> *Acacia decurrens*, Black Wattle.
> *Andira inermis*, Angelin.

Calophyllum walkeri, Kina.
Cedrela serrulata, Red Toon.
Cinnamomum camphora, Camphor.
Cupressus knightiana.
Cupressus macrocarpa.
Eucalyptus amygdalina, Peppermint Gum.
Eucalyptus diversicolor, Karri Gum.
Eucalyptus marginata, Jarrah.
Eucalyptus obliqua, Stringy Bark.
Eucalyptus robusta, Iron Bark.
Eugenia jambos, Jambu.
Grevillea robusta, Silky Oak.
Inga laurina, Spanish Ash.
Mesua ferrea.
Michelia nilagirica.
Myroxylon toluifera, Balsam of Tolu.
Tecoma leucoxylon, White Cedar.

(for tropical, sub-tropical, and warm temperate regions, according to species)

Abies species, Firs.
Acer pseudoplatanus, Sycamore.
Fagus species, Beeches.
Larix species, Larch.
Picea species, Spruce.
Tsuga species, Spruce.
Pinus species, hardy pines.
Pseudotsuga Douglasii et al.

(cooler and cold localities, selected according to appropriate conditions)

CARE AND MAINTENANCE

The upkeep of tree crops follows general agricultural and woodland care lines. Attention should always be paid to the provision of adequate fire-breaks at suitable intervals to ward off the risk of any conflagrations spreading, especially in dry regions or warm

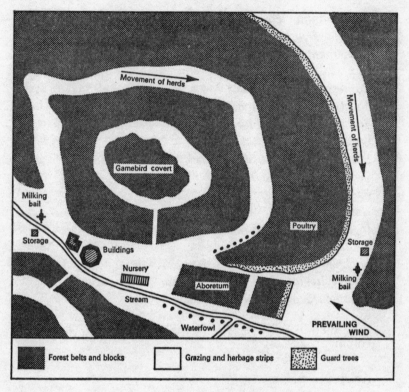

Fig 15. A typical layout with supporting facilities

summers. The elimination of any regeneration of useless and objectionable bush should be undertaken as necessary. Fences or barriers must be kept in good repair and if there are thorn or other hedges they should be controlled properly. By reducing such work to a minimum through skilful planning, the various tasks can be disposed of rapidly and without excessive labour. If any irrigation system has been installed, the channels should be maintained efficiently so that water can flow freely. For sloping land, a terracing method, consisting of contour banks arranged in series, is excellent. Check dams serve to retain moisture on the land and ensure that erosion does not occur, but they need occasional inspections to see that damage is not affecting their operation. In the same way, drains, whether surface or contour-aligned, should be cleared as necessary. Catchment pits, which trap soil that would otherwise be lost, have to be emptied periodically and the material spread on the land or carried to the nurseries for use in seed beds or transplanting containers. Pasture or open strips, too, should be kept free of coarse weeds and similar growth.

Good care and maintenance are essential to profitable agri-silviculture. It is quite purposeless to introduce high-quality tree crops to a new area and then fail to look after them adequately. This point has been emphasised consistently over many years by workers concerned with the development of marginal lands or the rehabilitation of degraded regions. Only too often work begins with enthusiasm and drive, but when the routine of regular super-vision and upkeep starts then the story becomes a different one. Persistent effort is vital to success. Although tree crops should not require laborious cultivations like those needed in arable culture, and work may be lighter and more interesting, there is a need for frequent and detailed checking of the progress and appearance of the crops. Moreover, tree growers must be quick to note any de-fects or changes in direction, and to rectify errors. In most ways, successful maintenance is largely a matter of commonsense and capacity for intimate observation of all parts of the forest farm. By its nature, estate work is many-sided, calling for versatility and ingenuity. Regular care makes daily duties light. In short, do not neglect any section and be up to date in maintenance activi-ties.

8

The Choice of Trees
i. Leguminous

AN ENORMOUS variety of productive, interesting and beautiful trees – many of them little known even to experienced foresters and orchardists – is available to the forest farmer of today. A careful study of tree literature will bring to light trees that will supply every nutritional need of human beings and animals as well as many other items of great commercial importance. There are trees that will supply fruit or nuts with the protein equivalent of the best quality meat or fish, tree-cereals, trees that provide edible oils, 'milk', and sugars, and trees whose leaves or shoots are as palatable as those of conventional vegetables. By tree-farming, in fact, communities could supply themselves with all their dietary requirements of proteins, carbohydrates, fats, minerals, vitamins and other nutritional factors, as well as their basic needs of fuel, clothing and shelter – and many profitable surpluses – without any of the arduous, expensive and uncertain processes associated with the cultivation of annual crops.

By modern plant-breeding techniques it has become possible greatly to increase the climatic range, productivity, palatability and nutritional content of traditional tree crops, so that the forest farmer, in any reasonably favourable area, can find varieties or cultivars which satisfy all his requirements. The development of new cultivars and hybrids has meant that bearing can begin far earlier than used to be the case. It is essential to select only fast-growing, high-yielding types. The usual procedure is to draw up check lists of required characteristics and relate them to the ecological conditions of the area of operation. Lists can then be drawn up of likely species of economic value, together with their growth requirements. By comparison, one can then see if these appear to be met by the conditions prevailing on the sites or which could be established there. The important point is to look for types known to thrive in similar places in other zones. Further study and evaluation should reveal some anticipated responses and probable profitability. In addition, by careful assessment of all collected data, it may be decided what extra facilities will be essential to support good development possibilities in the new sites. These detailed analyses and comparative studies can often save much trouble and expense, and may obviate costly failures.

Not only must the chosen species suit the growth conditions of an area, but they must also yield crops that are appropriate to the production that it is desired to establish in the forest farm concerned. Above all, it is vital that only the best seeds and planting material should be employed, obtained from proved high-yielding, quick-growing strains. To employ poor-quality stock is simply a waste of time. It costs no more to maintain a superior planting than a low-grade one and the returns from the latter will seldom be economic. It is no good thinking that you can get away with using inferior trees and plants in forest farming. You must take the same care in securing high-quality seeds and rootstocks or budding and grafting material for agri-silviculture that you would if you were an ordinary farmer raising cereals on arable land or sowing ground for leys and pasturage. A little extra effort in this direction at the start should reap rewards in the form of greatly increased dividends when the accounts come to be balanced.

It is convenient to divide the trees available for forest farming into six groups: tree legumes; nut-bearing; fruit-bearing; oil-producing; types suitable for livestock fodder; and miscellaneous. Grasses and other pasture constituents may be classified as grazing and fodder types.

Tree legumes have been used extensively in forest farming projects in many regions, as they can not only supply large quantities of highly nutritious cereal-equivalent crops, with a protein content ranging normally from fifteen to twenty-five per cent, as compared with the six to fourteen protein content of common cereals, but also release nitrogen into the soil for the benefit of neighbouring plants. The roots of many leguminous species contain nodules which are the habitat of bacteria with the power of fixing nitrogen from the atmosphere; this is liberated when the roots decay, thus enriching the soil. Leguminosae are the second largest family of seed plants, containing some 600 genera with 13,000 species, and are cultivated throughout the world, in both the tropics and temperate zones.

ACACIA

This genus groups together several hundred species very widely distributed throughout the warmer regions of the world, especially in the dry areas of Australia and Africa. The leaves of acacia trees are normally bipinnate. In some instances, and often where the locality of origin is very arid, the leaflets are suppressed, their stalks or petioles being flattened and having the physiological functions of leaves. These stalks are arranged vertically, such orientation serving to deflect intense sunlight and thus preventing injury by checking any excess evaporation of moisture from the green surface which might arise if the whole organ was exposed to scorching.

In general, acacias thrive in dry, sandy and hot conditions. The different species, sub-species and varieties produce a wide range of materials, from green fodder, pods and beans or seeds to gum, wattle bark, and perfume extract. Because the trees are suited chiefly to poorer land, they can perform useful functions in reclaiming gullies, stabilising stream banks, acting as wind-breaks, holding drift sand, giving valuable shade, making hedgerows and furnishing sources of firewood. Some types yield timber. In the Cape of Good Hope, large areas of sandy wastelands have been converted into usable condition by the planting of acacias. Nevertheless, the trees need keeping under control, since, if they spread too widely, they can often constitute a nuisance to some farming operations.

Acacia species are propagated normally by seed. There is often considerable variation in the quality of varieties of the same species and care should be taken to plant only seed from proved and selected trees. Three or four seeds may be sown together in the permanent planting sites, the strongest seedling only being subsequently allowed to grow on, or in containers in the forest nursery. As the outer coat or testa of most acacia seeds is very hard, the seeds should be placed in near boiling water and left to soak for two to three days before sowing. When it is possible to cut the seed with the thumb nail it will be soft enough to plant. Sometimes two treatments with hot water may be required to attain that condition. *Acacia arabica* or Babul can be found in the drier parts of tropical Africa, India, Sri Lanka and other areas. This tree yields the Indian gum arabic. Production in mature trees is about two pounds per tree annually. In Sind, the species bears lac. It is well suited to poor soils. The bark and pods are used for tanning and also as a dye in calico printing. The foliage gives good fodder and browse for livestock. *A. baileyana* is originally native to New South Wales and bears very long sprays of rich yellow flowers, with good foliage. The blooms are sold commercially in the holiday resorts of the western Mediterranean. *A. aneura*, together with *A. cibaria*, *A. longifolia*, and *A. oswaldi* yield useful pods and seeds which provide palatable foodstuffs. *A. longifolia* is popularly known as the Sydney golden wattle. It is a small spreading tree which blossoms twice yearly. *A. sphaerocephala* or bull's horn, is myrmecophilous, offering attractions for ant colonies; this constituting a drawback for practical usage. *A. hindsii*, indigenous to Central America, is very similar in characteristics.

The cutch or catechu tree of India (*A. catechu*) supplies a black gum resin, which is obtained by boiling chips of the heartwood. Catechu is astringent and is used for dyeing and tanning. One ton of the heartwood will yield about 250 to 300 pounds of catechu or cutch. One form of cutch is popular for chewing with betel leaf and a valuable gum is also obtained from it. The wood of *A. catechu* makes excellent charcoal, suitable for gunpowder. *A. concinna* supplies edible seeds which can be roasted; *A. leucophloea* yields both a hard and durable heartwood and seeds for milling into meal and flour. *A. cultiformis* is the knife-leaved acacia, with fine foliage. The silver wattle or mimosa tree (*A. dealbata*) is a small evergreen Australian species bearing large heads of fragrant yellow blossom. It makes good shelter belts from wind and is an excellent bee plant, as well as a source of tannin. *A. dealbata* is hardy and thrives in cold and exposed areas where the rainfall is over twenty-five inches annually. The firewood of this tree burns well. The Port Jackson or Australian wattle or willow

(*A. cyanophylla*) grows easily from seed, gives very useful fire-wood, reclaims drift sand and is most valuable for conservation and for forage. *A. cyclops*, also called the Australian wattle or willow, is very similar, as regards growth habits, habitat and uses. *A. karroo* or mimosa, suits very dry situations and hard soils. It is helpful in covering bare ground where other species may not grow initially. *A. litakunensis* or withaak is a flat topped medium-sized tree. It is drought-resistant and makes good fences, wind-breaks and hedges. *A. albida*, *A. heteracantha* and *A. lasiopetala* are other types appropriate for hot and dry regions.

The common or black wattle, also termed the green wattle (*A. decurrens*), is a handsome and quick-maturing tree of about forty to sixty feet in height, indigenous to eastern Australia, which will thrive in the tropics on most soils up to an elevation of 4,000 to 6,000 feet above sea level. The species is useful for green manur-ing and windbreaks. It yields good timber and first-class fuel. *A. decurrens* dislikes very heavy rains. Wattle gum is one of the products of this tree. For wattle bark production the variety or sub-species *mollissima* is planted commercially.

Mountain hickory or *A. elata* is another Australian species with open, feathery and drooping foliage. *A. farnesiana* is a small tree or shrub, common in the tropics and sub-tropics, which produces the cassie-flowers utilised in perfumery. *A. melanoxylon* or the Australian blackwood, is noted for its highly figured wood, em-ployed in cabinet making. The wood is durable and splits well for shingles. This species is a gross feeder and the roots spread long distances. It stands wind well but grows fairly slowly. The tree produces wattle bark commercially. *A. modesta* or phula is a small tree planted for hedges and browse. The umbrella tree or *A. planifrons* has branches which spread in a plane and an erect stem. The golden or broad-leaved wattle (*A. pycnantha*) is med-ium sized, with a bark rich in tannin. It attains a height of about forty to fifty feet and yields good timber. It is also a notable source of wattle bark.

A. senegalensis or true gum arabic is a small tree of the Sudan, which exudes gum naturally from the stem and branches. Exuda-tion is aided by incisions cut in the bark. It is also useful for for-age. *A. tomentosa* is the elephant-thorn tree or jungle nail, with thorns of three to four inches in length, while *A. tortuosa* or cushaw forms dense hedging for browse, under dry conditions. The Australian species *A. homalophylla* yields fragrant and decorative wood, and in Hawaii there is a species, the wood of which is excellent for making ukuleles, called the koa (*A. koa*). *A. seyal* or shittah is mentioned in the Bible, *A. armata*, with its heavily developed spines is the Australian kangaroo tree and *A. giraffae* is the African camel's thorn or the giraffe acacia. In Mauritius and Reunion, the species *A. heterophylla* is found, which yields forage and good timber. In Central America, in addition to the bull's horn, a similar type called *A. spadicigera* is common in certain areas.

Closely allied to the acacias are the *Albizia* species. *A. gummifera* and *A. lebbeck* suit hot and dry regions. The former is a large tree with fine foliage and excellent brown timber, which does not warp readily. It is also a host for the lac insect. *A. anthelmintica* is a small Arabian species, the bark of which is often used as a vermifuge for livestock. The sau tree or *A. moluccana* is quick growing and furnishes soft wood for making packing boxes, as well as fuel. *A. odoratissima* has very hard dark brown heartwood, while *A. stipulata* resembles the sau tree but is distinguished by its reddish coloured stipules.

Apart from their general merits, if used with discretion and under careful control, many of the acacia species are invaluable for initial plantings on bare ground or wastelands and sandy dunes. Once they are established they can create suitable conditions for the introduction of other species. In this way the acacias act as pioneers in the preparation of difficult lands for forest farming.

ALGAROBA (*Prosopis species*)

There are many species and types of algarobas. Most favour warmer climates, but some kinds are frost-hardy. The trees originate in South and Central America and the West Indies, though stands can now be found in many other parts of the world. Said to be more nutritious than corn by those farmers who cultivate them, algarobas are normally medium-sized trees, commonly yielding crops of brownish-yellow pods, something like wax beans in shape and size, extremely palatable, and with a fresh cereal odour. The sweet pulp contains about twenty-five per cent grape sugar, together with up to seventeen per cent protein. The pods or beans are a good livestock feed and are also consumed by some peoples. Algarobas have many uses: apart from their yields of foodstuffs, the wood is a satisfactory fuel, the lumber is used for piles, and the pale yellow flowers which are borne on long cylindrical spikes are the source of delicious honey. The best varieties are thornless, very quick-growing, being capable of bearing pods within two years after setting out. It is most necessary to choose seed with care. The bark contains tannin, and also a gum suitable for varnish and glue, as well as medicine for dysentery. Algaroba species mostly tolerate dry waste places thriving on light sand. When ground into meal or flour, the beans become a substitute cereal of delightful taste similar to maizemeal. One species, *Prosopis spicigera*, or the sami tree, growing in north India, is sacred to the Hindus. *P. africana* seeds are used in some parts of Northern Nigeria for food; *P. dulcis* pods are esteemed in South America as cattle fodder, and the seeds ground into powder are an important part of the diet of human beings in certain areas of Brazil. In Argentina, there are plantations grown in colder areas under irrigation for the raising of crops of algaroba beans as stockfeed. *P. juliflora* often has roots extending up to 100 feet below the surface of the ground, and can resist great drought. In the United States, there are six species of algarobas, and as many as fifteen in Argentina. Often two crops of beans can be produced in a year, and yields of high-quality plantings sometimes exceed twenty tons an acre annually. Owing to the extensive root development, it is necessary to keep strict control of plantations. Hawaii has thousands of acres under algaroba, and substantial benefits have resulted through its introduction there. The screw bean (*P. strombocarpa*) or tornillo, is also a useful species. It is important to select good-quality seed of superior strains. Several authorities have undertaken improvement work with this forest crop, notably the Department of Forestry, Hilo, Hawaii; the Arizona Agricultural Experiment Station, Tucson, Arizona; Ministry of Agriculture, Buenos Aires, Argentina; and the United States Department of Agriculture. Bulletin No 13 of the Arizona Agricultural Experiment Station discusses the use of the algaroba or mesquite as a fodder crop.

BAUHINIA

The seeds of *Bauhinia thonningii*, a small tree of tropical Africa, are eaten by certain peoples in the Sudan and similar areas. *B. esculenta* bears edible pods, which are much liked as an article of diet. It is a woody plant and often cultivated.

CAROB (*Ceratona siliqua*)

This is a small to medium-sized tree, originally native to the eastern Mediterranean, but now cultivated throughout the sub-tropics, especially in Queensland, California, parts of North India and to some extent in South Africa. It has pinnate leaves and bears heavy crops of sweet, sugary pods from six to ten inches in length, nearly one inch broad, dark brown in colour, and very palatable. These pods are a valuable food for farm livestock, but are also relished by human beings. Commonly termed 'beans', they contain over fifty per cent sugar, and may be eaten whole or ground into meal and flour. Such products are excellent for incorporation in baby milks and foods, for diabetics and other invalids and for employment in a number of industrial processes. Carob seeds yield gum of commercial quality and can be used as a substitute for coffee. The sweet, mucillaginous pulp from the beans is sold as a confection called St John's Bread. The tree is dioecious generally and in cultivation it is essential to graft selected varieties on to strong seedling stocks. Alternatively, male trees may have branches inset from a good female tree reserving two or three male branches so as to ensure pollination. In seedlings, the tap roots are delicate and must not be exposed or handled. The species is especially important to the economy of Cyprus, where large gum factories utilise the seeds for the making of adhesives for export. Unimproved carobs can be slow growers, but the new cultivars begin to bear at three to four years after planting out and yields may be as much as 1,000 pounds of pods per tree. Carobs thrive on rocky and stony land in arid and semi-arid regions. The productive life of trees is about 100 years. Harvests of up to twenty tons an acre annually are known in carob plantations.

Winter temperatures of −8°C or below will cause injury and in general even slight prolonged frosts can retard fruiting. For these reasons, carobs are not recommended for cropping in areas where the climatic conditions are too cold. Neither do they like excessive dampness, but are rather noted for their drought-resisting qualities and ability to utilise underground water supplies. For livestock feeding, carob beans have been found slightly superior to barley.

FOOD INGA (*Inga edulis*)

This tree is cultivated in tropical parts of the Americas for the fleshy, edible pulp yielded by the pods. The seeds, too, are some-times eaten, but they remain rather tough and leathery even after prolonged boiling. Several other *Inga* species are grown through-out Mexico and Central America and produce nutritious beans or pods. *I. laurina*, or Spanish ash, makes a good shade tree for cocoa and other crops.

HONEY LOCUST (*Gleditsia triacanthos*)

This valuable tree legume, well suited to cooler zones, can be found in North America from Ontario down to Texas. It has also been naturalised in Europe and introduced into parts of Africa. The trees bear pods or beans (about twelve to eighteen inches long containing a sweetish succulent pulp, with a content of twenty-seven per cent or so of sugar) which are relished by farm livestock and sometimes eaten by human beings. Honey locusts are of at-tractive appearance, have strong and durable wood, and are in addition rapid growers. They have fairly open top foliage, are regular in bearing habit, and can be propagated either by root suckers or seed. Grafting, too, is frequently practised. By employ-ing superior cultivars, high yields may be secured, of the order of up to 1,000 pounds of beans per tree a year. The pods curl slightly when dry and make an excellent meal or flour. *Gleditsia triacanthos* is frost-resistant, and will thrive without difficulty on lighter soils, the roots penetrating deep down into the ground. The merits of this species for hilly districts are considerable. Be-cause of the open canopies formed in plantations of honey locusts, it is possible to underplant with shorter kinds of trees to form a secondary productive layer. Grass, too, will grow satisfactorily under honey locusts. Another species, G. *japonica*, is native to Japan.

Among the advantages offered by honey locusts in forest farming and for schemes of multiple usage, may be listed rapid growth, improvement of the soil, high production of cereal-substitutes, regular bearing, and easy harvesting of beans or pods. Work on the species has been carried out at the Experiment Station at Hays in Kansas, as well as at the Department of Horticulture in Fort Hope, Ontario, Canada. The United States Department of Agriculture has also given attention to the selection of superior types of honey locusts.

INDIAN BEECH (*Pongamia glabra*)

This tree bears glossy pinnate leaves, which make excellent livestock fodder. The timber is good and the juice of the roots has antiseptic properties. A native of the Indian sub-continent. The flowers are creamy white and very pleasantly scented.

JEHEB-NUT (*Cordeauxia edulis*)

This is a small desert tree which grows north and east of the Sahara. The one-seeded pods, which are borne profusely, form a palatable 'bean'. Fruiting begins when the trees are only about three feet in height and continues as they develop to full size. The seeds or beans are eaten as dry legumes in Somaliland and other countries. They can be ground into a nutritious meal for livestock.

NAMNAM (*Cynometra cauliflora*)

This species is a shrubby, spreading tree with small bipinnate foliage, and a native of South-East Asia and India. The fruits are in the form of large, thick, fleshy pods, rather arc-shaped and produced in large numbers on the trunk near ground level or on the lower portions of the branches. Pods are green and yellowish-green in colour, about half an inch thick and up to some three inches in length, with a taste similar to unripe apples. Namnam thrives in moist, low-lying regions on deeper soils. Pods can be dried and ground into meal or flour.

OWALA (*Pentaclethra macrophylla*)

A tropical African tree, the seeds of which, after roasting or boiling, are used as food. An oil is also extracted from the beans. The raw seeds contain a poisonous alkaloid, called paucine, but this is removed by soaking and cooking, as is done in the case of some varieties of cassava.

PARKIA

These trees may be found in fairly moist areas in southern Asia and Africa. Many of the species are noted for the pods or beans and nuts which they bear, which are of good quality and make excellent and nutritious foodstuffs. The leaves also provide useful forage for livestock. Types such as *Parkia africana*, *P. speciosa*, *P. roxburghii*, *P. biglandulosa* and *P. filicoidea* are well worthy of much more extensive planting, with progressive breeding and selections of improved strains. Several institutions in various areas are interested in the development of *Parkia* species for cropping in forestry and farm work and enquiries for seeds could be directed to such authorities as the Forest Research Institute, Selangor, Malaysia, or African agricultural and forestry departments in tropical areas of that continent. The fruits of *Parkia* species are often called nittanuts and African locust beans.

POLYNESIAN CHESTNUT (*Inocarpus edulis*)

This species grows in the Pacific islands. The large, fleshy seeds, one or two to a pod, taste like ordinary chestnuts and are an important food in Tahiti, Samoa, and neighbouring places. The tree has also been introduced to areas of southern Asia. It grows to moderate size and has large shiny leaves. The native name is kayam.

RAIN TREE (*Pitheolobium saman*) AND RELATED SPECIES

This tree, as well as the Jering (*Pitheolobium jiringa*) which is also called the Guango, Inga and Penikaral, was introduced from tropical America to South-East Asia about the middle of the nineteenth century. It has a rather shallow root system and grows rapidly. The brown, flattish pods, about six to eight inches long, contain a quantity of sweet, sugary pulp, and are relished by cattle and other animals. Quantities are exported from South America for livestock feeds. The tree has small pinnate leaves, which form a canopy of shade in the daytime but close up at night, so that during a period of drought a patch of green grass may be seen beneath the branches while the surrounding ground is parched and dark. This led to the superstititon that the tree mysteriously produced rain at night, hence its popular name. *P. jiringa* thrives on fair soils in drier regions, but it can attain very great size in hot, moist regions. After drying, the pods make an excellent meal when ground up in hammer mills. In Indonesia the seeds of *P. lobatum* are eaten in many areas. It is customary to bury them for several days, after which they are washed and the sprouts cut off and thrown away. Steeping the raw grains in salt water for two hours is also practised. When fried in oil, the treated seeds can make a pleasant dish. *P. dulce*, or Madras Thorn, also bears edible pods. This species is drought-resistant.

SESBANIA GRANDIFLORA

This is a small, erect, quick-growing, soft-wooded tree, which attains a height of from fifteen to twenty feet. It bears large pendulous flowers. Both the fleshy petals as well as the tender leaves can be eaten, while the immature pods are used as a vegetable. *Sesbania aculeata* is a prickly shrub, common in south-east Asia, the dry seeds of which are sometimes consumed. The plant is annual and it also yields a strong and durable fibre, suitable for ropes and cordage. *S. aegyptiaca* bears pale yellow flowers and grows to a height of about eight to fifteen feet, according to local conditions. All the above noted, as well as other types, may be found in cultivation in different areas, both for foodstuff and for green manuring.

TALLOW TREE OR DATTOCK (*Detarium senegalense*)

This tree is common in parts of tropical Africa, and includes both savannah and forest varieties. The fruits of the former kinds are eaten either fresh or dried. The seeds are edible, or the oil can be extracted for human consumption and the residues employed as animal fodder. The trees furnish excellent timber, often called 'African mahogany'. The crops consist of masses of small one-seeded pods with farinaceous pulp of sweet nature, which can be dried and milled into meal. The bitter kinds should be avoided. Dattocks are tall and handsome in appearance.

TAMARIND (*Tamarindus indica*)

This is a large tree, probably a native of India, which is now cultivated in many warm areas. The pulp of its pods, pressed and preserved in large masses, is commonly sold in eastern bazaars and is the tamarind of commerce. It is sweetish-acid in flavour. The seeds contain oil and can be ground into a palatable meal. Tamarind is also used to make cooling beverages, as a seasoning in chutneys and preserves, and as a native medicine. The trees are drought-resistant, yield a termite-proof timber and bear brownish coloured pods. The leaves are small and pinnate, and the blossom reddish-yellow.

TREE LUCERNE (*Cytisus species*)

These are small leguminous types, mainly appropriate to higher elevations in the sub-tropics. They produce heavy yields of valuable livestock fodder. The leafy branches can be cut and fed directly. *Cytisus proliferus*, or Tagasaste, is indigenous to the hills of the Canary Islands, where it is appreciated for cattle farming. Normally two harvests are taken annually. Other species are *C. stenopetalum* and *C. pallida*, bearing yellow and white flowers respectively. The plants all require fairly light friable soils.

VELVET TAMARIND (*Dialium ovoideum*)

These tall trees are normally found in dry, semi-arid districts of Sri Lanka and neighbouring lands. The fruits are dark brown, small, and velvety, each being about the size of a hazel-nut. The shells are thin and brittle, containing one or two seeds, surrounded by a sweet/sour farinaceous pulp. The timber is red in colour and handsome. The pulp is often sold in the markets, and when dried forms a good stockfeed. Another type, *Dialium guineense*, with larger leaves, grows in West Africa.

WHITE POPINAC (*Leucaena glauca*)

A medium-sized species, robust, quick-growing, and drought-resistant, the white popinac is a native of tropical America and the West Indies, but now flourishes in many hot zones. It is also known as lucena. The trees mature rapidly and furnish good fuel; their foliage is relished by cattle, and the young fruits are eaten in the East Indies and parts of Africa by human beings. The ripe seeds are edible as well and when roasted are used as a substitute for coffee. *Leucaena glauca* can be spaced closely, if necessary, to give ground cover. Normally, the trees attain a height of from fifteen to twenty feet and the leaves, which are of fine bipinnate shape, make excellent green manure or compost. Lucena seeds should not be fed to pigs and horses, but they are suitable for cattle, sheep, and goats. It is reported that swine have become bald after eating them. *L. esculenta* is another useful species, confined to Mexico, where both the pods and the mature seeds are consumed.

9
The Choice of Trees
ii. Nuts

NUTS ARE of great commercial importance in the world economy. Some are rich in carbohydrates and many rich in proteins. Altogether about 105 kinds are utilised for foodstuffs in various countries.

ALMOND (*Prunus amygdalus*)

There are many varieties of sweet almonds. The nuts are high in protein – eighteen to twenty per cent – and have excellent calcium values. If the nuts are used as food the skin should not be removed because the concentration of calcium and iron in the skin is three times that in the kernel. *Prunus amygdalus* is a species of the temperate zones, belonging to the family Rosaceae, and it thrives in places with a chalk sub-soil, or where lime can be supplied. In exposed localities, the plantations should be protected from strong winds by belts of guard trees. Ground almonds form a popular item in human diet, and for livestock rations the whole seed should be milled.

BEECH (*Fagus species*)

Various species of beech trees are indigenous to the northern hemisphere and yield useful crops of nuts or 'mast'. The American beech or *Fagus grandifolia* and the European beech, *F. sylvatica* are well known. American beech is suited to fairly dry sandy and loam soils. There are recognised varieties or sub-species such as *pubescens, ferruginea* and *caroliniana*, growing in various areas from New Brunswick down to Florida. European beech has a large range from Sweden and Norway to the Mediterranean and from Russia to Iran and Asia Minor. In England, the mast or nuts of the beech were a common animal feeding-stuff; in fact the county of

Buckinghamshire derived its name from the formerly famous forests of beech growing there, the old name of beechmast being buck (Old English, *boece* or *bece*). In France, beechmast is used for feeding pheasants and fattening domestic fowls. The nuts also yield about seventeen to twenty per cent of a non-drying oil suitable for lighting, cooking or as a substitute for salad-oil and butter. Varieties or sub-species of European beech include *atropunicea*, or the copper beech; *laciniata* or the cutleaf beech; and *pendula* or the weeping beech.

Japanese beeches include *F. japonica* and *F. sieboldii*, which have been now introduced into other areas. Antarctic beeches, belonging to the genus *Nothofagus*, are widely distributed in the Antipodes and South America.

Beeches are also noted for their valuable timber and the leaves form good forage.

BRAZIL-NUTS (*Bartholletia excelsa*)

Belonging to the family Lecythideae, this species grows under cultivation in South America and is indigenous to the basins of the Amazon and the Orinoco rivers. The trees are tall, have long pointed leaves and need a hot, moist climate with deep alluvial soils. The fruits or nuts possess hard brown shells in which are enclosed up to fifteen seeds – the Brazil-nuts of commerce. The thick shells must be crushed to extract the nuts, and to make milling easier the seeds should be kept at freezing point for a few hours before grinding. Brazil-nuts contain fourteen per cent protein and some sixty-five per cent fat. Unimproved strains are slow growing. *Lecythis zabucajo*, or paradise nuts, are closely allied to brazil-nuts, but possess a better flavour.

BREAD-NUT (*Artocarpus incisa (var.)*)

This is a seed-bearing variety of the breadfruit tree, common in the West Indies. A solid, white fleshy mass is obtained from the fruits which, on roasting, resembles the crumbs of a new loaf. It may be ground into meal or flour, and constitutes, as does the bread-fruit proper in the South Pacific, an important article of local diet. Propagation is by seed, or preferably by root suckers and layering. Bread-nuts and bread-fruits belong to the family Urticaceae.

CASHEW-NUT (*Anacardium occidentale*)

The fruits of cashews consist of two distinct parts: the pear-shaped stalk or 'apple' about three to four inches long, and the nut, grey or brown in colour, and some one to one and a half inches in length. The shells of the nuts should not be used. Shelling is not difficult and the seeds can be ground or milled quickly. The trees are of spreading habit and medium size, being indigenous to tropical America and the West Indies, but have for long been naturalised in Africa and Southern Asia. An intoxicating drink is obtained in some areas by distillation of the hypocarp, while an insect-repelling gum can be obtained from the species and an indelible ink from the juice of the bark. Cashews thrive in moderately dry districts up to an elevation of about 3,000 feet above sea-level. The nuts are important in commerce today. They constitute a nourishing foodstuff, containing eighteen per cent protein, forty-eight per cent fat, and a fair quantity of carbohydrate. The taste is excellent. The species belongs to the family Anacardiaceae. With good management and choice of superior strains, plantings can be very productive.

CHERONJI (*Buchanania latifolia*)

Mainly a mountain tree, common in south India along the Western Ghats. It has simple leathery leaves and belongs to the family Anacardiaceae. The species bears pear-shaped nuts, regarded as substitutes for almonds. A fine oil can be expressed from them.

CHESTNUT (*Castanea species*)

Chestnuts have for centuries played an important part in the forest and agricultural economies of many nations. The trees are notable food producers, prolific seeders and, once established, are capable of withstanding considerable drought, owing to their deep rooting systems. Loose, porous and moderately dry soils, slightly acid or neutral, provide the best growing conditions. The bark and wood of chestnuts are rich in tannin and the wood has many uses. Modern chestnut cultivation is concentrated on the growing of blight-resistant types and hybrids, in areas where the chestnut blight is a problem.

The main kind of chestnut trees are: American chestnut (*Castanea dentata*), which was abundant in the eastern areas of the United States, before the introduction of the chestnut blight, especially in the Appalachian mountains; Chinese chestnut (*C. mollissima*), common in Northern China and Korea, and grown in other areas, noted for its well formed and tasty nuts; European chestnut (*C. sativa*), the commercial tree of many countries, with a growing range from Scotland to India and Northern Africa to the Caucasus; Japanese chestnut (*C. crenata*), indigenous to Japan and Korea but introduced into North America, bearing nuts of slightly coarse nature tasting somewhat like a sweet potato. The Japanese chestnut is really a mountain species and is an abundant fruiter.

Castanopsis (*Castanopsis* species), from which come castanopsis nuts, are evergreens suited to warmer conditions and are originally native to South-East Asia and California. They produce nuts similar in taste to a cross between an acorn and a chestnut. *Castanea alabamensis*, the Alabama chinquapin of the South-Eastern United States, yields edible nuts and timber. Other chinquapins include *C. pumila* or the Allegany, water or dwarf chestnut; *C. ashei*, the Ashe chinquapin; *C. floridana*, the Florida chinquapin; *C. henryi*, the Henry chinquapin, a Chinese species; the Ozark chinquapin or *C. ozarkensis*; and the trailing or creeping chinquapin, *C. alnifolia*. All these produce nuts for food purposes, but the trailing chinquapin is mainly of botanical interest.

Numerous varieties of chestnuts may be obtained for commercial production. The Chinese chestnut is not as well known as it should be amongst foresters and farmers. This species grows at high elevations, is of squat habit with a large spreading crown, thus being easy to harvest and care for in plantations or belts in agri-silvicultural projects. Popular varieties include: Bartlett, Carr, Hobson, Milford, Reliance, Stokes, Yankee Crane, Orrin and Zimmerman, from naturalised American stocks, as well as others. Hybrids of different chestnut species are becoming ever more important in forest and commercial plantings.

Selection of the appropriate chestnut varieties for cold conditions offers valuable scope for forest farmers in harsher climates. Chestnuts show great capacity for vegetative reproduction through the development of vigorous and numerous coppice sprouts. These arise from the root collar after removal of the bole in harvesting.

COCONUT (*Cocos nucifera*)

Well known for its copra, the source of coconut oil, this species is cultivated throughout the tropics. It is a palm tree. There are numerous varieties and some, such as the dwarf types, yield nuts within four years after planting out. Desiccated coconut averages three and a half per cent protein. Fed with moderation, it is a useful supplementary ration ingredient for livestock. The trees also provide fibre, timber, thatch and material for making domestic utensils, apart from the uses of coconut in the soap-making, margarine and other industries. A warm and humid climate is essential for the growing of *Cocos nucifera*.

In north-eastern Tanzania, coconut cultivation is integrated with cattle rearing, with excellent results.

COUNTRY ALMOND (*Terminalia catappa*)

This is a medium-sized spreading tree, indigenous to Malaya, but commonly found in other areas of southern Asia. The fruits contain kernels, which are edible and of good flavour. The species bears two crops annually, followed by two periods of leaf fall. It will thrive from sea-level to an elevation of about 2,000 feet. Propagation is normally by seed. The leaves are leathery and of large size. *Terminalia okari* or the okari nut, is native to New Guinea and yields nuts measuring about three inches long by three quarters of an inch in diameter. The produce is important locally, constituting a valuable item of diet. Both species are therefore the sources of useful foodstuffs. They belong to the Combretaceae. *T. belerica* also yields edible seeds.

FILBERT OR HAZEL (*Corylus* species)

These are temperate-zone species in general, some being quite large trees while others are low shrubs. Filberts are a very important nut-bearing group of plants of commercial significance. The chief types include:

BOTANICAL NAME	POPULAR NAME	ORIGIN AND USES
Corylus americana	American filbert or hazelnut	Eastern North America. Edible nuts
C. cornuta	Beaked filbert	Eastern North America Edible nuts
C. californica	Californian filbert	West coast of the United States. Edible nuts
C. chinensis	Chinese filbert	Central and west China Edible nuts and timber
C. avellana	European filbert, hazelnut or cobnut	Europe Edible nuts
C. maxima	Giant filbert	Edible nuts
C. ferox	Himalayan filbert	Himalaya mountains Edible nuts
C. sieboldiana	Japanese filbert	Japan Edible nuts
C. americana × *C. avellana*	Mildred filbert hybrid	United States Edible nuts
C. heterophylla	Siberian filbert	Siberia, China and Japan Edible nuts
C. colurna	Turkish filbert or Constantinople hazel	Turkey, southern Russia & Himalayan mountains Edible nuts and timber

Commercial cultivation: In Asia Minor, Europe and the United States, the European and giant filbert species are popular, many economic varieties being grown. There are also useful varietal selections well known locally in Asia, Siberia and China. The European filberts or hazels seldom attain heights exceeding twenty-five feet, but the Turkish filbert can grow to sixty feet and the Chinese type to as much as 120 feet tall. European filberts prefer a cool climate, with a definite period of winter chilling and a deeper, fairly rich medium soil. The main damage to the trees may be caused by strong cold winds and this can be prevented in forest farming by windbreaks of various suitable species guarding the filbert belts or blocks. The roots penetrate quite deeply into the ground. Moderate shade is desirable and filberts make a good second-storey crop under an open canopy of larger economic trees.

In England, the practice is to prune hazels hard in the late winter after the pollinating period is over and then again in summer by controlling new shoots. In the United States, less pruning is done, but the branches are opened up to permit sunlight to reach all fruiting spurs, with strict control of suckers. Pollinisers are planted at regular intervals in filbert groves, allowing one polliniser to every five or eight fruiting specimens.

The American and the beaked filberts or hazels have been hybridised with the Europen types to breed hardier varieties which thrive in northern areas. Important work in this connexion has been carried out at the United States Department of Agriculture and the New York State Experiment Station.

Varieties: Well known English cultivars include the Kentish Cob, an oblong, wide and thick nut of excellent quality; and Prolific or Frizzled, a very heavy cropper which ripens early, with as many as twelve nuts in a cluster. Kentish Cob does well in quite stony soils. American varieties such as Barcelona and Du Chilly are popular, Royal is a giant-fruited variety of Oregon, while excellent hardy types are available for commercial cultivation in Germany. Turkish, Italian and Spanish cultivars are also good yielders.

Treatment: Where there is time available to exploit the food-bearing qualities of filbert groves, the young trees may be left to develop freely for the first year or so. Then the branches should be cut back to an outward bud, to form a basin-shaped bush with about six strong shoots, which in due course will give rise to twelve main branches. In turn, these will produce laterals in number, which when shortened, will be the fruit bearers. Older trees develop under this system into a squat formation, measuring some twenty feet across by not more than six feet in height. Harvesting then becomes very simple. Long shoots are removed annually, to maintain a horizontal shape to the trees or bushes and sold for basket making. Reproduction of stock is normally by detachment of ground suckers, which are planted in the forest nursery where they should root satisfactorily in a season. Nut bearing should commence in about the third year after planting out of the trees.

HICKORY OR PECAN (*Carya* species)

Hickory or pecan trees generally prefer a sub-tropical climate, with drier conditions, being indigenous to the temperate areas of North America and China, but they can withstand winter frosts and often bear fruit as far north as latitude 45° (equivalent to cultivation in say, Vermont, Bordeaux, Croatia, Southern Russia, Vladivostok, or British Columbia). The trees also grow in various parts of Australia and South Africa. Because of the number of different species and varieties available the scope for the use of hickories or pecans in forest farming is considerable. It is, however, necessary to select the right types for differing situations, since pecans respond most favourably to the climatic requirements that may be appropriate to the given species or strain of tree.

Hickory and pecan nuts are an important commercial food crop, of considerable nutritional value and good flavour. Noteworthy species include:

BOTANICAL NAME	POPULAR NAME	ORIGIN AND USES
Carya cordiformis	Bitter hickorynut	Originally native to the Eastern United States and Ontario, useful for timber only
C. texana	Black hickorynut or Buckley hickory	Originated in Texas, Oklahoma and Arkansas, supplies edible nuts and fuel
C. carolinae-septentrionalis	Carolina hickorynut or southern shag	South-eastern United States. Supplies edible nuts and timber.
C. cathayensis	Cathay hickorynut	Native of China. Source of edible nuts and timber
C. fernowiana	Fernow hickorynut	Common in South-western United States. Edible nuts and timber
C. ashei	Hammock hickorynut	For timber and fuel

BOTANICAL NAME	POPULAR NAME	ORIGIN AND USES
C. tomentosa	Mockernut hickorynut, bigbud hickorynut or bullnut	Found in eastern United States and Ontario. Source of edible nuts and timber
C. myristicaeformis	Nutmeg hickorynut	South-western United States. Edible nuts and timber
C. glabra	Pig hickorynut or hognut	Eastern United States and Ontario. Nuts or mast for feed and timber
C. ovalis	Red hickorynut or false shagbark	Eastern United States and Ontario. Edible nuts and timber
C. pallida	Sand hickorynut or paleleaf hickory	South-eastern United States. Supplies nuts or mast for feeding and timber
C. floridana	Scrub or Florida hickory	Native to Florida. Fuel
C. ovata	Shagbark hickorynut, Little scalybark or Tuscatine	Eastern United States and south-east Canada. Edible nuts and timber
C. laciniosa	Shellbark hickory, bigleaf hickory, bottom hickory or big scalybark	Indigenous to the central and eastern United States. Supplies edible nuts and timber
C. leiodermis	Swamp hickorynut	Found in Louisiana and the Mississippi area. Edible nuts and fuelwood
C. tonkinensis	Tonkin hickorynut	Native of southern China and north Vietnam. Supplies edible nuts and timber
C. aquatica	Water hickorynut or bitter pecan	Found in southern areas of the United States. For fuel only

BOTANICAL NAME	POPULAR NAME	ORIGIN AND USES
C. illinoensis	Pecan or Illinois nut	Southern United States, but also grown in Michigan, British Columbia, Vermont, southern Ontario, and northern Mexico. Naturalised in New South Wales and Natal (South Africa). Supplies the pecan nut of commerce. The annual production of pecan nuts in the United States alone is over two hundred million pounds.
C. oliviformis	as for C. illinoensis	
C. illinoénsis × C. laciniosa	Pecan × Shellbark hybrid or Hican	Found in Indiana, Illinois and Iowa. Nuts

Hickorynuts and pecans are important food crops and in addition the timber of many species is valuable, being both tough and elastic. In general, the trees prefer deeper and more friable soils. Modern plant-breeding techniques have developed groups of different varieties suited to particular climatic zones. The hickorynut crops were known to the American Indians, who gathered them as forest produce long before the arrival of the white immigrants. Some cultivation of grafted pecan varieties began in Louisiana in the 1840s and by 1890 several important cultivars were introduced, followed by extended commercial production in the southern United States. To secure good nuts, pecans normally require high summer temperatures without a great fall in temperature at nights.

Notable varieties of pecans include :

South-eastern United States: Brooks, Candy, Curtis, Desirable, Elliott, Farley, Mahan, Moore, Stuart and Success.
Western United States: Clarkesville, Giles, Greenriver, Hirschi, Major, Peruque, Posey, Starking and Witte.

Maryland: Duvall, Sweeney.

Central Texas: Barton, Burkett, Clark, San Saba Improved, Squirrel, Texhan and Western.

For colder areas: Hican hybrids such as Burton, Des Moines, Henke, Jay Underwood. McCalister is a good pollinator. Lingenfelter is a good variety of shagbark hickorynut.

New and improved varieties are being continuously introduced to cultivation.

JAVA ALMOND (*Canarium commune*)

This species bears heavy yields of fruits almost all the year around, which have edible kernels resembling sweet almonds. It thrives in hot and moist tropical areas up to 2,000 feet above sea-level, requiring a deep, well-drained soil. The nuts or seeds are tasty, and also produce a useful cooking oil. Considerable amounts were exported from the Philippines. *Canarium commune* is a good plantation tree. It belongs to the family Combretaceae.

OAK (*Quercus* species)

Acorns have been used as a standard food since the earliest times. Different species vary considerably in their characteristics, some bearing nuts comparatively quickly, others growing swiftly and also possessing great productive capacity. Acorns are palatable generally, but even when tannin is present it can be easily removed. Their food value is excellent. Oaks belong to the family Fagaceae, and there are over three hundred species known, very widely distributed in the temperate zones. *Quercus ilex*, or the evergreen oak, has been known to yield crops of 2,000 pounds of nuts in a single season. The cork-oak tree (*Q. suber*) is, of course, famous for its bark, which can be stripped for collection every nine to twelve years, but in addition the species produces edible acorns and timber. In south-central Portugal, local farmers practise multiple-usage forestry, obtaining three benefits from the cork-oak woodlands – timber, cork-bark, and meat from the pigs which feed upon the harvest of nuts. In the vast cork-oak estates, sheep and goats browse upon the bushes, tree foliage, and grass ground-cover, while herds of swine consume the acorns and herbage. The pork found at Evora, in the province of Alto Alemtejo, is especially good, and it is all produced by animals fed on oak crops. *Q. suber* can flourish on sandy and stony ground, which frequently comes within the classification of barren or marginal lands. The English oak (*Q. robur*), the Turkey oak (*Q. cerris*), and the American species *Q. alba* and *Q. virginiana* are other valuable types. Considerable scope exists for the selection and planting of material chosen from well-known, high-yielding, quick-growing individual trees. After grinding, acorns make an excellent meal which is liked by farmstock. The drawbacks of some strains lie in the fact that production can vary in alternate years, but this may eventually be overcome by careful arrangement of forest stands so that the blocks and belts maintain a constant yield, some being at maximum in one year and others in succeeding seasons. However, as a long-term forage crop, oaks have few equals if properly managed, and they also give very superior timber. In addition to the species already mentioned, the black oaks, *Q. trilobata* and *Q. rubra*, as well as the post oak, *Q. minor*, are heavy yielders.

Oaks are widely distributed in the northern hemisphere. They are, of course, well known for their excellent timbers. Acorns have been used for feeding purposes from ancient times in different parts of the world. The genus *Quercus* may be divided botanically into three distinctive groups, termed the *Cyclobalanus*, *Leucobalanus* and the *Erythrobalanus* oaks. In *Cyclobalanus* trees, the involucral bracts of the acorn cups are fused together in concentric rings, but in the other two types the bracts are spirally arranged. *Leucobalanus* types are known generally as white oaks and *Erythrobalanus* are the black or red oaks. Oaks with evergreen foliage are often called live oaks.

Some valuable species include :

American oaks: *Q. alba*, or the white oak; *Q. macrocarpa*, the bur oak; *Q. stellata*, the post oak; *Q. prinus*, the chestnut oak; *Q. michauxii*, swamp chestnut oak; *Q. lyrata*, the overcup oak; *Q. rubra*, the eastern red oak; *Q. velutina*, the black oak; *Q. shumardii*, the Shumard oak; *Q. coccinea*, the scarlet oak; *Q. phellos* or willow oak; and *Q. virginiana*, the live oak. The Gambel oak (*Q. gambelii*) grows in the Rocky Mountains, while in Arizona the Arizona white oak (*Q. arizonica*) may be found. Oregon white oak (*Q. garryana*, California white oak (*Q. lobata*), California black oak (*Q. kelloggii*), the interior live oak (*Q. wislizenii*), canyon live oak (*Q. chrysolepis*), the California live oak (*Q. agrifolia*) and the California scrub oak (*Q. dumosa*) are other notable types.

Mediterranean oaks: *Q. suber*, the cork oak; *Q. ilex*, the evergreen holly oak.

Eurasian oaks: The brown oak or *Q. robur* is the English oak, but also grows from western Europe to the Caucasus. *Q. cerris* is the Turkey oak, found in the mountains of Asia Minor and Southern Europe. It can also be seen growing in England and the Eastern United States.

Other useful species are the Kermes oak (*Q. coccifera*), indigenous to the Mediterranean basin; *Q. aegilops*, found in Greece and on the Levantine coasts; and the Aleppo oak or *Q. infectoria*.

Various other types of trees, not related to *Quercus* species, are often given the popular name of oak. These include the silky or satin oaks of Australia; the tulip oaks, also of that continent; the shee, beef and flame oaks of the genus *Casuarina*, and African oaks.

In Great Britain, *Q. robur* is called the common or pedunculate oak. This species has hybridized with *Q. petraea*, the sessile oak, to produce *Q. rosacea*. *Q. borealis* is locally called the red oak. It has a sub-species or variety, *maxima*. *Q. rubra* can also be seen, as well as *Q. cerris*.

PALMYRA PALM (*Borassus flabellifer*)

The soft kernels of the nuts of *Borassus flabellifer*, when young, are much used as foodstuffs. The trees prefer a dry climate with warm conditions. They are dioecious, and produce the toddy of south India.

PEACH-NUT (*Bactris utilis*)

This is a palm tree, much cultivated in parts of central America and Equador for its crops of fruit. The product resembles a large date, and the flesh is like that of chestnuts. Peach-nuts are highly nutritious, and make an excellent meal after drying. The trees are slender and spiny and the leaves are pinnate in form. Each one can yield about 150 pounds of fruits annually. The species is suited to low and medium elevations and needs warm conditions.

PINE (*Pinus* species)

Here we have a large number of economic trees of much value in forest farming, especially for their yields of foodstuffs, timber and other items. Pine trees of different types are widely distributed in all areas of the world. The most important nut-bearing species include:

European and Asian: P. *halepensis*, the Aleppo pinenut; P. *pinea*, a Mediterranean species, popularly called the Stone or Italian stone and Pignolia pine. P. *cembra*, the Swiss stone pinenut, called Pignolia, which extends across Siberia. P. *griffithi* or blue pine, is similar to P. *pinea*, but is native to the Himalayan mountains, thriving at altitudes of about 7,000-12,000 feet above sea level.

Chinese: P. *bungeana*, lacebark pinenut, indigenous to north-western China.

Japanese and Korean: P. *koraiensis*, the Korean pinenut.

North American: P. *cembroides edulis*, Colorado pinyon; P. *coulteri*, Coulter pinenut; P. *sabiniana*, digger pinenut; P. *jeffreyi*, Jeffrey pinenut; P. *flexilis*, the limber pinenut; P. *cembroides*, the Mexican pinyon; P. *cembroides parryana*, Parry pinenut; P. *ponderosa*, Ponderosa pinenut; P. *cembroides monophylla*, single-leaf pinyon; P. *lambertiana*, the sugar pinenut; P. *torreyana*, Torrey pinenut or soledad; P. *monticola*, the western white pinenut; P. *albicaulis* or the whitebark pinenut; P. *quadrifolia* or Parry pinyon.

South American: Araucaria araucana, the Araucarian pinenut, piñon or pinyonie, a native of Chile.

Pine seeds or nuts are borne in the axils of the cone scales. The export on a commercial scale of the nuts of Italian stone pines or pignolia has for long been an important industry, but the nuts of other *Pinus* species are chiefly consumed in their local growing areas, for both human and animal feeding purposes.

P. sylvestris or the Scots pine, make an excellent nurse or guard tree crop for other species, which can grow up sheltered by the conical growth of the strong and hardy pine trees. The species withstands wind and sea gales very well.

Planting and propagation techniques for pine trees are well established and leaflets or booklets on the management and care of these coniferous species may be obtained from many local forestry authorities in different countries, especially those in which the various types may be indigenous.

PISTACHIO NUT (*Pistacia vera*)

This is a small tree, indigenous to Asia Minor, and much cultivated in the Near East and Central America for its nuts. When roasted, these have a pleasant aromatic flavour. They can be ground into a fine meal. The species belongs to the Anacardiaceae. Only good cultivars should be planted to secure high output.

QUEENSLAND NUT (*Macademia ternifolia*)

This species is native to North-East Australia, and is of moderate size, with dark green narrow leaves. It yields hard, round nuts of agreeable flavour. Propagation is usually from seed. The nuts must be crushed before grinding into meal, owing to their hard smooth shells. *Macademia ternifolia* belongs to the family Proteaceae.

SOUARI-NUT (*Caryocar nuciferum*)

A species, native to the Guyanas, which bears fruits containing up to five seeds or nuts each. The trees prefer warm and moist conditions, with deep alluvial soil or loam. The nuts have excellent flavour and about sixty per cent fat. *Caryocar tomentosum* is very similar, but quicker growing, yielding crops within five years after planting. It is indigenous to Brazil. These species belong to the family Caryocaraceae.

WALNUT (*Juglans species*)

Practically all walnut trees furnish some foodstuff in the form of nuts, which are eaten by wild animals, farm livestock or man. Commercial cultivation of the various types constitutes an important world industry and the *Juglans* species form a valuable section of forest-farming projects, wherever their planting may be appropriate. In addition to nuts, walnut trees yield timber of beauty and much popularity.

The chief species and types are:

South American: Juglans australis (Argentine walnut), *J. boliviana* (Bolivian black walnut), *J. honorei* (Ecuador walnut), *J. columbiensis* (Columbian walnut).

Central American: J. insularis (Cuban walnut), *J. mollis* (Guatemalan walnut).

Chinese: J. cathayensis (Cathay walnut), *J. mandshurica* (Manchu walnut).

Japanese: J. sieboldiana (Japanese or Siebold walnut).

European (or Persian): J. regia (Circassian, European, Persian, *et al.*, walnut).

North American: J. major (Arizona black walnut), *J. nigra* (American walnut), *J. cinerea* × *sieboldiana* (Bixby walnut), *J. californica* (California black walnut), *J. hindsii* (Hinds walnut), *J. nigra* × *regia* (Intermediate walnut), *J. californica* × *nigra* (Nigornica walnut), *J. hindsii* × *nigra* (Nigrind walnut), *J. nigra* × *sieboldiana* (Nigroldiana walnut), *J. regia* × *sieboldiana* (Notha walnut), *J. cinerea* × *regia* (Perbut walnut), *J. californica* × *regia* (Regifornica walnut), *J. rupestris* (Texas walnut).

Miscellaneous: The heartnut or cordate walnut (*J. sieboldiana cordiformis*) is a native of Japan. The Butternut or the Long or White walnut (*J. cinerea*) grows in the eastern United States and South-east Canada.

Various alternative local names exist for many of the above-mentioned species.

CULTIVATION: The Persian or European walnut has been grown for many hundreds of years in various countries. It is said to have been planted by the Romans in Great Britain prior to the second century A.D. Introductions from different areas have been made into North America for some time. For commercial purposes, walnut trees are headed so that the height does not normally exceed twenty feet. The secrets of successful management and production are to use high-quality varieties or cultivars, graft on to stock of the same species, employ pollinisers, aim for regular spacing with about a dozen to fifteen trees to the acre, and ensure control of weeds, pests and fertilisation. Heading the trees low also provides shade for the trunks and helps to bring on full bearing at an early date. The nuts should be harvested normally when about ten per cent of the hulls have broken open, the rest can then be loosened, if desired, with ethylene gas or the water sweat process. Prompt hulling and drying will give better produce for sale or for milling into meal.

Valuable varieties of European walnuts for commercial forest work include: Eureka, Placentia, Mayette, Concord, Franquette and Payne. Much work on the development of high-class walnut varieties has been done by the California Walnut Growers' Association, the East Malling Research Station in England, the University of California, the United States Department of Agriculture, the California Agricultural Experiment Station and the Oregon Agricultural Experiment Station. The University of Nanking also pioneered the breeding and propagation of walnuts. Varieties of *J. regia* highly resistant to snow and severe cold can be found in the mountainous areas of Asiatic Turkey.

The American or eastern black walnut (*J. nigra*) is grown commercially in the eastern United States. The Northern Nut Growers' Association has sponsored the development of new selections. Popular cultivars include: Allen, Adams, Creitz, Edmunds, Edras, McMillen, Myers, Ohio, Sifford, Snyder, Stabler, Stambaugh, Tasterite, Ten Eyck, Thomas, Todd and Wiard. Both hand-driven and motorised shellers may be employed to hull the nuts. On farms, a standard potato peeler and a hosepipe delivering water will shell and clean black walnuts rapidly. They can then be ground into meal for stockfeed. The Arizona black walnut bears a small nut which is suitable only for stockfeed. The Californian black walnut is of similar value. Hinds walnuts are of good quality, equal to the American or eastern black type.

Heartnuts or cordate walnuts, originally of Japanese origin, are suited to moderately severe northern regions, grow rapidly and develop a broad and low-spreading crown with luxuriant foliage. The heartlike nuts split readily after harvesting. Notable varieties are: Bates, Lancaster, Stranger, Walters, Wright and Fodermaier. Siebold walnuts are larger than heartnuts, but more difficult to crack.

The Texas black walnuts are shrubby and small trees, with small round nuts. These are sweet, but only suitable for livestock feeding. South and Central American walnut species, with their hybrids, still await further development. The Chinese walnuts are well suited to cold northern climates.

Butternuts or long white walnuts are hardier than the eastern black walnut and thrive in the North-eastern United States and Canada.

Because of their growth habits, walnuts can be often under-planted with ground crops of legumes and grasses without any difficulty or with smaller economic food and forage trees and shrubs. If well chosen and good species and varieties are planted and where necessary sheltered with lines of guard trees, the plantations will thrive in quite harsh conditions. The eastern black walnut, for example, has done well under winter temperatures of as low as $-5\,°C$, while certain strains of the European walnut and the Chinese walnuts withstand far greater cold.

VARIOUS NUT TREES

The following list identifies a further number of different species which yield nuts or comparable products, often used locally or internationally for foodstuffs and various raw materials which may be of additional interest to forest farmers or for multiple-usage projects.

BOTANICAL NAME	POPULAR NAME	ORIGIN AND USES
Pyrularia pubera	Allegany oilnut or elknut	Eastern North America
Bunium species	Arnut or earth chestnut	Western Europe to the Caucasus. Feeding-stuff
Orbignya oleifera	Babassunut	Brazil. Valuable for food purposes and fuel oil, with other uses

BOTANICAL NAME	POPULAR NAME	ORIGIN AND USES
Jatropha curcas	Physicnut	Indigenous to tropical America. Medicinal only
Morfinga oleifera	Bennut	Caribbean and India. The oil is employed by artists and portrait painters
Areca catechu	Betelnut or arecanut	Eastern Pacific, naturalised in other areas. This is a masticatory nut
Brosimum alicastrum	Breadnut	Tropical America. Used for foodstuff. May be boiled or roasted
Aleurites moluccana	Candlenut	Pacific islands. Oil is manufactured from candlenuts
Gevuina avellana	Chilehazelnut	South-western south America. Used for feeding purposes
Cyperus esculentus	Chufanut	Southern Europe. A useful food for pigs
Ophalea triandra	Jamaican cobnut	Caribbean and tropical America. Employed as foodstuff
Attalea cohune	Cahounnut	Central America, notably Honduras. The nut yields an oil for making soaps and margarine
Cola acuminata	Colanut	Western African species. Used for beverages and food. It is a stimulant
Jubaea spectabilis	Coquitanut	South-western south America. Yields an oil for soap making
Irvingia gabonensis	Dikanut	West Africa. Useful foodstuff. Also produces oil
Attalea funifera	Coquilla	Piassava palm of Brazil. The tree yields fibre

BOTANICAL NAME	POPULAR NAME	ORIGIN AND USES
Aesculus hippocas-tanum	Horsechestnut	Europe. Starch may be obtained from the nuts. Not edible
Simmondsia chinensis	Jojoba nut or goatnut	China, California and Mexico. Foodstuff. The oil from the nuts is a good hair-dressing. Has also been used as a substitute for whale oil

10

The Choice of Trees
iii. Fruit, Oil and Fodder

FRUIT TREES

FOR FRUITS for human consumption, reference may be made to numerous standard works on horticulture; but, in the context of forest farming it is important to note that many fruits can also be used for livestock feeding. Apple-pulp, for example, has been suggested as a component of cattle-feeds; on the continent of Europe grape and olive residues are used for this purpose, and both figs and dates provide valuable fodder. The forest farmer might consider the cultivation of such fig trees as *Ficus benjamina*, *F. caponsis*, *F. sycomorus* and *F. rhodesiaca* in the appropriate areas.

BOKHARA PLUM (*Prunus bokhariensis*)

A member of the rose family, *P. bokhariensis* is generally cultivated in the Punjab, Afghanistan, and the surrounding areas. The chief merit of the fruits is that they can be dried easily and form an excellent foodstuff. The trees grow vigorously. Large amounts used to be exported from Kabul into India. However, there is much variation between individual trees and selection is important for high and consistent yields.

CANDLE TREE (*Parmentiera cerifera*)

A small tropical American tree, which bears cylindrical, fleshy, candle-like, yellow fruits along the stem and branches. The crops appear twice yearly and in great profusion. The fruits are up to twenty inches in length and are eaten locally. They can be dried for stockfeed. *P. cerifera* belongs to the family Bignoniaceae.

HAWTHORN (*Crataegus* species)

Hawthorns are shrubs or trees of the genus *Crataegus* belonging to the rose family (*Rosaceae*) and widely distributed in North America, Europe, North Africa and Asia Minor. They are not known south of the Equator. The wood of hawthorns is hard, they respond to trimming and cutting, make good hedges and barriers and bear small fruits resembling miniature apples. The foliage serves as useful forage. In certain cases, serious efforts are being made to select improved types of notable species which yield larger fruits suitable for livestock fodder. When dried, these can be milled into a nutritious meal for feeding purposes. There are probably over one thousand *Crataegus* species recorded today.

Some notable types include *C. oxyacantha* and *C. monogyna* which are well known in Great Britain, bearing the common names of may, whitethorn or hedgerow thorn. The fruits of these species are called haws. The Washington thorn or *C. phaenopyrum* produces red fruits and grows in the South-eastern United States. *C. calpodendron* or pear haw, is native to Eastern north America and has orange-red coloured fruits. The cockspur thorn or *C. crus-galli*, a shrubby tree, is indigenous to eastern north America and bears red fruits. *C. lavallei* is a hybrid type, while *C. arnoldiana* flourishes in the north-east area of the United States, producing pear shaped and brick red fruits. The red haw or *C. mollis* is a tree of the central United States, with scarlet fruits, each about one inch in thickness.

C. stipulosa or manzanilla, and *C. orientalis*, are natives of Guatemala and Mexico in Central America, yielding valuable fruits, suitable, when dried or fresh, for animal feeding and for making into tarts and preserves when ripe.

Hawthorns are quite simple to propagate vegetatively. Extensive collections of *Crataegus* species may be found at Arnold Arboretum of Harvard University in Massachusetts in the United States.

JACK-FRUIT (*Artocarpus integrifolia et al.*)

The seeds of the jack-fruit as well as the large fruits themselves, make excellent cattle food, and other livestock relish them. Further useful species include:

SPECIES	PRODUCT
Artocarpus lakoocha	Edible seeds
A. nobilis	Pulp for drying and making into meal, and edible seeds
A. odoratissima	Sweetish pulp. Seeds
A. rigida	Pulp and seeds

Artocarpus species are tropical trees, suited generally to warm and moist areas. The seeds and dried pulp can be ground into meal for farm animals, or the fruits may be fed in fresh condition with advantage. There are many varieties and care should be taken to select good quality cultivars or strains.

MULBERRY (*Morus* species)

Mulberry species are distributed in northern temperate regions and in the subtropics or cooler mountainous tropical areas. They are deciduous trees or shrubs and possess many advantages for forest farming. In general, the trees are easy to propagate, grow rapidly, bear very early, give regular crops, have long fruiting seasons, and recover speedily from any frost damage. The mulberries produce both fruits and forage, not to mention the value of the wood for fencing-posts or fuel. Reasonable planting distances for most mulberries are about twenty-five to thirty feet apart each way. In colder areas, such as northern Scotland, the trees need shelterbelts alongside plantations for the best results. Propagation is normally by cuttings or layers.

Morus rubra or the North American mulberry produces dark red berries. The black mulberry (*M. nigra*), originally native to Western Asia, was cultivated by the ancient Greeks and Romans and was well known in Northern Europe as early as the ninth century A.D. The fruit is purple-black in colour. *M. alba* or the white mulberry, which bears near-white fruits, is of ancient Chinese origin. This is the chief species utilised in silkworm culture. Formerly, *M. nigra* was employed in sericulture in Italy, but was superseded by the white mulberry in the fifteenth century A.D. The varieties or sub-species of white mulberry include *multicaulis* or the Philippine mulberry, and others. The Philippine type is much esteemed.

Indian mulberry or *M. indica* yields small red cylindrical fruits of poorer flavour, but which are palatable to animals and birds. Apart from their valuable fruits, which can be dried and ground into meals for livestock feeding, the leaves of mulberries are an important fodder.

Broussonetia papyrifera, the paper mulberry, an allied species, yields bark for paper and cloth making. The leaves are large and ovate and edible.

PANGI (*Pangium edule*)

A native of Malaya, this species produces large brownish-red ovoid fruits about six inches in length. The fruits can be dried for animal feed, while the seeds, if boiled to remove the hydrocyanic acid present, are edible too. They also yield a useful oil. Pangi belongs to the family Bixaceae.

PERSIMMON (*Diospyrus* species)

Persimmons are trees of a very large climatic range. There are hundreds of economic varieties and cultivars available to growers. As a crop for use in forest farming, the persimmon has the advantages of extreme tolerance as to soil conditions, since different types can thrive on all sorts of land ranging from sand to clay. The trees are not usually discouraged by poor soils. The fruiting season is long and prolific bearing occurs before they reach a height of six feet. In the United States, commercial production of persimmons is well established in California. In the Gulf states, the trees are common in private gardens. Many species and varieties are frost resistant, but do not generally withstand temperatures below $-18°$C.

Persimmons have great merits as a food crop. Important species include:

BOTANICAL NAME	POPULAR NAME	ORIGIN
Diospyrus kaki	Oriental persimmon	China and Japan, introduced into Europe and the United States
D. virginiana	Native American persimmon	Atlantic coast to prairies of North America

BOTANICAL NAME	POPULAR NAME	ORIGIN AND USES
D. chinensis		China
D. conazotti		Mexico
D. sonorae		Mexico
D. rosei		Mexico
D. lotus	Date plum	Common in Italy

Superior varieties of persimmons for commercial planting have been developed by the Bureau of Plant Industry of the United States Department of Agriculture over many years.

OIL-PRODUCING TREES

Fixed oils often constitute worthwhile and important products, whether for local and domestic use or for sale. Various trees yield such oils, as well as food and other products and because many of these species are less well known, some suggestions are given below for planting in forest farming.

BOTANICAL NAME	POPULAR NAME	ORIGIN AND USES
Amoora rohituka	Hingul	A moderately sized Sri Lankan species, belonging to the family Meliaceae. The seeds produce oil that can be used for lighting and other purposes
Argania sideroxylon	Argan	This is a Moroccan tree and is cultivated in the Maghreb. The seeds yield an oil for cooking equivalent to olive oil and both the leaves and fruits make excellent stockfeed. Family Sapotaceae
Azadirachta indica	Margosa or neem	The Indian neem tree which produces an aromatic oil of medicinal value. Foliage edible. Family Meliaceae

BOTANICAL NAME	POPULAR NAME	ORIGIN AND USES
Balanites manghamii	Manduro	Native to Mozambique. The nuts yield a clear oil, which burns well. Family Simarubaceae
Balanites aegyptiaca	Desert dates	Indigenous to the drier areas of West and Central Africa. Edible fruits and seeds yield betu or zachun oil
Bassia butyracea	Indian butter tree	Grows in Central India at from 1,000 to 5,000 feet above sea level. Thick oil or fat which resembles butter or ghee is produced by the seeds. The flowers yield a syrup from which spirits or sugar may be prepared. Family Sapotaceae
Bassia latifolia	Mowra or mahua	Also common in central India. Mowra fat is obtained from the seeds, used for cooking, the manufacture of soap and chocolates and in margarine
Bassia longifolia	Mee	Found in Sri Lanka, India and Malaya. Has fleshy seeds, which yield arippu oil, used in cooking. An alcohol can be prepared from the edible flowers. Mowra cake and arippu cake, left as residues after the extraction of the oil from the fruits or seeds, are excellent fertilisers, but are not edible
Calophyllum inophyllum	Punnainut	Indian species. A medium sized tree, which yields a medicinal and burning

BOTANICAL NAME	POPULAR NAME	ORIGIN AND USES
		oil from the nuts. It is dark green and scented. Collected in Sri Lanka as forest produce
Calophyllum tomentosum	Keena	Grows in moist and higher areas of Sri Lanka, the West Indies and Malaya. The seeds yield an orange-coloured oil used for medicinal and domestic purposes. Keena oil is exported. Another and larger species is *C. walkeri*
Carapa guianensis	Carapa	This species bears large fruits from which crab oil is extracted. The oil is used in medicine and for other purposes. Native to the Guyanas
Diospyros embryopteris	Tunka	Indian species. Medicinal oil
Dipterocarpus glandulosus	Doranatel	A tall erect tropical tree of Asia. Resin exudes from the stem which yields a medicinal oil
Dumoria heckeli	Bakonut	A tropical West African species. Large smooth seeds, edible and rich in oil. May be used also for making soap
Garcinia echinocarpa	Madotel	A small tree of the tropics. The seeds yield a medicinal oil
Gynocardia odorata	Gynocardia	Tree of the eastern Himalayan foothills. Seeds yield gynocardia oil
Hydnocarpus anthelminticus	Kavatel	Medium-sized species of Indian sub-continent

BOTANICAL NAME	POPULAR NAME	ORIGIN AND USES
H. wightiana		Medicinal oil. The above four species belong to the family Bixaceae
Irvingia olivera	Dika or caycay	A tree of Vietnam, similar to *I. gabonensis*. Yields nuts rich in fat and edible. Family Simarubaceae
Kokoona zeylanica	Kokun	A large tree of south India. The seeds yield an illuminating oil. Family Celastraceae
Lophira alata	Kiam	The scrubby oak of Sierra Leone. Kiam or meme butter is produced from the seeds. Family Dipterocarpeae
Moringa pterygosperma	Moringa or horseradish tree	The horseradish tree often grown in gardens in India and Sri Lanka. It attains a height of about twenty-five feet. The roots can be eaten as a substitute for horseradish, the leaves are suitable as a vegetable, as well as for pickles and seasoning, and the long unripe pods may be boiled and sliced like green beans. The flowers and bark are medicinal and oil of Ben is obtained from the seeds. Propagated by seeds or by cuttings.
Pentadesma butyracea	Tallow or butter tree	A large tropical West African species which bears oblong fruits up to six inches long and three

BOTANICAL NAME	POPULAR NAME	ORIGIN AND USES
		and a half inches in width. The large fleshy seeds contain oil, known as koma or okoto oil. A heavy fruiter, giving about 150 to 200 pounds of seed a tree annually. Family Guttiferae
Quillaja saponaria	Quillai	A Chilean species, the bark of which is saponine. Known as vegetable soap. Family Rosaceae
Sapindus emarginatus *S. saponaria*	Penela soapberry	Tree of Indian sub-continent. Small tree of Caribbean, notably Jamaica. Both trees are saponaceous, the fruits when fresh or dried making useful soap substitutes
Schleichera trijuga	Ceylon oak or kusumb	Tree of Indian sub-continent. The edible seeds are rich in oil
Taraktogenos kurzii	Kalaw	Native to Burma and Thailand. The seeds yield chaulmugra oil, used for treatment of leprosy. The tree is cultivated in Hawaii
Trichilia emetica	Malfura	An East African deciduous species which bears nuts rich in oil. This is edible and can also be employed in making soaps and candles. The residue after extraction is not edible but can be used as fertiliser

EUCALYPTS

The *Eucalyptus* species constitute very valuable types for afforestation in certain areas. Apart from timber and shelter, these trees in a number of cases yield quantities of commercial oil, which can be included as a cash product in forest-farming operations, as well as famine fodder in some instances.

Generally, *Eucalyptus* species for oil production are grown more closely than for timber, while it is often customary to keep the trees or 'bushes' to low heights to facilitate leaf harvests. This demands variation of planting and maintenance techniques, but the value of the ground cover afforded by the plantations is in no way diminished for normal conservation purposes. It often pays to produce oil rather than timber, so provided the markets are available it can be quite an attractive proposition for foresters and farmers.

Eucalyptus species vary in the climatic and soil preferences to some extent and account has to be taken of the local habitats when arranging introductions. Within these guidelines it is just as easy to plant high oil-yielding types as to use other species and varieties. Farmers interested in eucalyptus oils would profit by visiting growing regions, both existing and projected or new ones, and when armed with the necessary information, will be in a position to assess the prospects of securing useful and marketable oils from new areas. Almost everyone is acquainted with the popular eucalyptus oils, but there are many valuable species yielding equally interesting oils that are not so well known, nor indeed properly assessed yet. These might be of importance if more attention were paid to their characteristics and qualities.

Itinerant harvesting and field distillation of *Eucalyptus* species, as practised in natural stands of the trees or sometimes on forested lands, often means that the essential oils of several species are mixed up together. This gives the product a degree of variation and accounts for the unreliability of many lots. Quality can also be reduced and buyers are never quite sure of what they are purchasing, despite sampling. In pure stands of cropped trees in bush form on well laid-out modern farm plantations consistent yields of standard quality may be secured regularly. It is greatly to be desired that every possible effort to raise the purity and quality of eucalyptus oils should be made. This can be done best by plantation culture, selection of the most superior strains, good weeding and trimming and satisfactory plant husbandry. The crops need efficient management and skilful field care, harvesting at appropriate times and elimination of haphazard practices, which lower oil quality. By producing only high-quality oils of recognised purity and value, forest-farmers can contribute immensely to the improvement and extension of all types of eucalyptus for the production of the best essential oils as profitable sections of agrisilvicultural enterprise in suitable areas. (For a list of eucalypts, see Appendix III.)

FODDER TREES

COW-TREE (Brosimum galactodendron)

This is a large tree, belonging to the family Moraceae, and native to tropical America. It yields copious amounts of a latex resembling cow's milk, which is wholesome and nourishing. It can form a useful feed for young stock, especially calves and pigs.

GNETUM GNEMON

A medium-sized species, belonging to the family Gnetaceae. It is native to South-East Asia, where it is often cultivated. The seeds can be boiled or roasted and are commonly sold in the markets. The leaves and flowers are also edible. G. gnemon is a useful all-round forage tree in tropical areas.

JUJUBE (Zizyphus jujuba)

This tree is suited to dry areas, and bears fruit profusely. The seeds are large and the pulp surrounding them becomes farinaceous on drying, being utilised in parts of Africa and China for making porridge and bread. There are several varieties and propagation is by grafting or layering. The plant also acts as a host for the scale insects producing lac. Z. jujuba yields a valuable cereal substitute and owing to its ability to thrive in rather arid regions is of considerable economic importance. It belongs to the family Rhamnaceae. The trees are small, of spreading habit and thorny, but it may be possible to select and multiply thornless stocks.

KEI APPLE (Dovyalis caffra)

A small thorny tree, very resistant to heat and drought. The foliage makes useful fodder, often constituting a helpful supplementary ration for livestock in bad seasons. The species is also valuable for hedges and in windbreaks.

LETTUCE TREE (*Pisonia alba*)

This small evergreen species is specially adapted to sea coasts. It can be propagated easily by cuttings. The leaves are eaten as a vegetable in southern Asia, while they also provide a good source of cattle forage. The colour of the foliage is pale yellow, of rather striking appearance. *P. alba* belongs to the family Myctagineae.

MAIDENHAIR TREE (*Gingko biloba*)

This handsome species, native to China and Japan, but also naturalised in other temperate countries of slightly warmer climates, yields edible seeds which are relished in east Asia. It is not suited to very hot tropical areas. *G. biloba* belongs to the Gingkoaceae. The seeds can be milled to form a useful livestock feed. The trees have crowded fern-like leaves. They are deciduous, prefer deeper soils and shelter from strong winds.[1]

MAPLE (*Acer* species)

The maple family contains some two hundred trees and shrubs in two genera: the Dipteronia, two species, of central and south China; and *Acer* or true maples. The maple species are widely distributed in the northern hemisphere. In general, the Aceraceae offer useful sources of forage and all maples yield a sweet watery sap. Types of notable interest include:

Western North American: Big-leaf maple (*Acer macrophyllum*) is a commercial species supplying an important hardwood which grows from Alaska to southern California on the Pacific coastline. The vine maple or *A. circinatum* is an understorey type of the same area. Small American mountain species include *A. negundo*, the box elder; *A grandidentatum* or big-tooth maple; and *A. glabrum* or the Rocky Mountain maple.

Eastern North American: These may be divided into hard, soft and mountain groups. Hard maples of note are *A. saccharum*, which provides timber, forage and maple sirup; *A. barbatum* or

---

[1] Often known as a 'living fossil', the Gingko is a relic of an early geological period, before the advent of flowering and fruiting species.

the Florida maple and *A. leucoderme* or the chalk maple, both small trees; and *A. nigrum* or the black maple, a supplier of timber. *A. saccharum* is found from Newfoundland to North Dakota and down to Georgia and Texas. It can attain a height of ninety feet and has hard pinkish wood. The black maple is indigenous to the North-eastern United States and the Great Lakes area. Soft maples include *A. rubrum*, the red maple, and *A. saccharinum*, the silver maple. The red maple possesses leaves which are silver-white below, is a rapid grower, of medium size and has flamboyant crimson autumn foliage. The silver maple grows chiefly east of the Great Plains. Understorey species of the northern American forests such as *A. spicatum*, the shrubby mountain maple, and *A. pensylvanicum*, the striped maple, are well known.

Europe and Western Asia: A. campestre, the hedge maple, is indigenous to Northern Europe and Western Asia. It is a small tree, up to twenty feet in height, and is called the common maple in Great Britain, where it can be seen in hedgerows. A useful forage species. *A. pseudoplatanus* is the sycamore or sycamore maple, which provides timber. The juice of this species is not milky. *A. platanoides* or the Norway maple, with its variety or sub-species *schwedleri*, has greenish red to reddish bronze leaves and a milky juice or sap. Both the sycamore maple and the Norway maple grow to between forty and sixty feet in height.

Asiatic types: The small Chinese maple or *A. truncatum*; *A. ginala*, the dwarf maple; *A. palmatum* and varieties of the Japanese maples; and *A. carpinifolium*, or the hornbeam maple, are noteworthy species.

Maple sirup is a valuable product of the sugar maple and the black maple, which deserves to be more widely appreciated and which could be introduced into more areas. The crop was known to the American Indians long before the arrival of the white settlers in North America. Maple sirup is the sap or sweet water yielded by the trees. The extraction of this juice is a commercial enterprise in the North-eastern United States and Eastern Canada. The sap contains one and a half to three per cent of solids, mostly sucrose. It is concentrated by evaporation in open pans, thus imparting good colour and flavour to the product. From thirty to fifty gallons of the maple juice will provide one gallon of saleable sirup. Modern methods, including the establishment of central evaporation plants serving whole communities of sap tappers and producers, have placed the industry, which is a good example of a forest production system, on a sound basis in North America. Maple sirup is used in table sirups, in confectionery manufacture, in ice-cream toppings, and as a flavouring in cigarette tobacco. It can also be substituted for molasses in stock feeding.

SAL (*Shorea robusta*)

Indigenous to India and popularly known as the sal tree, this species can be called a multi-purpose type. The ground-up husk of the seeds makes a good animal feeding-stuff. Other products include oil for confectionery and fat for soap making. The leaves are suitable for forage. The related species of *S. talura*, called jalla or jalari, is also of importance. *S. oblongifolia* is a native of Sri Lanka and yields a clear resin or damar, used in varnishes. These trees belong to the Dipterocarpeae and grow mainly in moister forested areas or at lower elevations. The sal tree is now being exploited commercially in Eastern India.

SALT-BUSH (*Atriplex* species)

There are several valuable fodder shrubs belonging to these species, including *A. semibaccata* and *A. nummularia*. They thrive on sandy soils in arid districts and provide useful forage for livestock, especially at times of drought. The plants are palatable and free seeding. *A. repens* is another good species often seen on sandy shores. They are members of the family Chenopodiaceae.

WEEPING WILLOW (*Salix babylonica*)

This graceful tree is frost-resistant, with drooping branches, and though it grows well on stream banks it can also withstand drier conditions in sub-tropical regions. The species originates in Asia Minor. It is easily propagated by cuttings. The foliage makes excellent livestock fodder. *S. subserrata* is similar but smaller, and flourishes on stony sites along gullies and watercourses. *S. persica*, which spreads freely from suckers, can be found in many areas of Persia and Iraq. All the species belong to the family Salicaceae.

MISCELLANEOUS

BOTANICAL NAME	POPULAR NAME	ORIGIN AND USES
Litchi chinensis	Lycheenut	South China. Grown in many areas. Foodstuff. The raisin-like pulp surrounding the seed is eaten as a fruit, but the whole can be dried and milled into feeding-stuff. Much esteemed in China
Semecarpus anacardium	Marany or marking-nut	Indian species. The juice of the nuts is used for making ink and varnish or caulking material. Edible seed which yields oil
Castanosperum australe	Moreton bay chestnut	Australia. Useful food
Aleurites montana	Muyuoilnut	South China. Oil for manufacturing purposes
Myristica fragrans	Nutmeg	East Indies. Spice
Telfairia occidentalis	Oysternut or tabui	African species. Useful food
Elaeis guineensis	Palmnut	West Africa. Oil
Garcia nutans	Pascualitonut	Central and Northern South America. Yields a hard and quick drying oil
Canarium ovatum	Pilinut	Tropical Pacific areas. Useful foodstuff. Nuts have excellent flavour
Fusanus acuminatus	Quandongnut	Australian species. A useful foodstuff
Ravensara aromatica	Ravensaranut or clove nutmeg	Malagasy. This is a spice
Lecythis zabucajo	Paradisenut or sapucaianut	Indigenous to tropical South America. Useful foodstuff

BOTANICAL NAME	POPULAR NAME	ORIGIN AND USES
Ocotea spp.	Sassafrasnut	South America. An aromatic nut. Spice
Butyrospermum parkii	Sheanut	African species. Valuable for foodstuff and oil for soap-making. Grows in west tropical parts of the continent. Medium sized tree bearing large fleshy nuts with high percentage of stearine fat. Used locally in cooking, for chocolates and for candles. Popularly called shea butter
Sapindus saponaria	Soapnut	Caribbean area. Can be used for washing purposes
Phytelephas macrocarpa	Ivorynut	Central America. For making buttons
Sapium sebiferum	Tallownut	China. Yields wax for soap and candles
Aleurites fordii	Tungnut	Indigenous to south China, but grown commercially elsewhere. Yields tung oil for paint and varnish making. Not edible
Trapa natans	Water chestnut	South China. Used for food
Eleocharis tuberosa	Waternut	South China. Useful foodstuff

The lists in this chapter and the two previous chapters are not, of course, exhaustive and further valuable species may be available in different areas, often of some local significance.

11

Fields for Expansion
i. Temperate Uplands

VAST SCOPE exists for the application of forest-farming techniques in the development of those extensive areas of the earth's surface which are at present unexploited or grossly under-exploited, as far as food production is concerned, and whose potentialities must be fully explored if the bulk of the world's rapidly growing population are to lead tolerable lives.

Conventional farming systems do not possess the capacity to make the marginal and wasted lands fully productive, while it is clear that the comparatively small existing areas of fertile agricultural land are quite unable to produce, even with better strains of crop plants and improved cultural techniques, the huge quantities of nutriment which will be required to feed a world population that is expanding at the rate of some seventy-six millions a year. Harvests from trees tend to be far more abundant than those from conventional annual crops of cereals and vegetables, and in every continent there can be found immense regions where the growing of economic tree crops could well be the only practicable solution to the problems of development. Trees can thrive and bear on ground that is unsuitable for field grains. The path towards future extension work has been pointed out already by the trials and experiments of recent years. What is now wanted is much greater international effort, preferably coordinated through the United Nations Development Programme, particularly in the backward countries and in marginal areas. This should include the opening of stations for the further investigation of specific aspects of multiple-use forest farming, the intensive dissemination of advice and information, the provision of large quantities of high-quality seeds and planting material to farmers and foresters, and the establishment of projects for the breeding of additional improved varieties or cultivars of economic species. By such means the extension of forest farming would be greatly accelerated.

In developing arid areas, such as deserts, eroded agricultural wastelands, barren uplands, regions of primeval forest, bush or scrub, an early necessity is to create shelterbelts, so as to protect and conserve the soil and water supplies and provide favourable conditions for livestock, crops and human beings. In recent times several very large shelterbelts have been created. Some 200 million trees were planted in the Great Plains shelterbelt project conceived by Franklin D. Roosevelt and carried out between 1934 and 1943 in North and South Dakota, Nebraska, Kansas, Texas and Oklahoma, to save those areas from complete devastation in the Dust Bowl crisis. China has planted a shelterbelt 1,000 kilometres long and fifty kilometres wide to protect farmland in the north-east from encroachment by the Gobi Desert. Algeria is developing a thousand-mile shelterbelt in the east of the country to contain the Sahara. Already 30,000 workers have planted thirty million trees over an area of more than a million acres, mainly on the denuded flanks of hills, and the scheme envisages the planting of between ten and twelve million trees a year – a truly monumental anti-desert campaign.

While shelterbelts must of necessity comprise hardy species, there is no reason why, in many cases, economically valuable trees, including food-bearers, should not be included. Roosevelt's Great Plains shelterbelt included many honey locusts, and these in fact showed the highest percentage of survival, while India's Rajasthan shelterbelt, mentioned in chapter IV, consists largely of algarobas. There is no reason, in fact, why the belts of trees which are the principal feature of a forest farm should not be planted on shelterbelt lines.

British forestry experts, especially J. M. Caborn of Edinburgh University, have made many valuable suggestions as to the form and layout of shelterbelts. A well-designed shelterbelt should be an interlocking complex of diverse trees and shrubs, adapted to the topographical, climatic and soil conditions of its site. It should not be too dense, the aim being to filter the wind rather than checking it abruptly. Complete obstruction, forcing the wind upwards, causes turbulence and eddying, which may be particularly damaging to corn crops. A mixture of different species makes for resistance to disease, frost, drought and fire and is more beneficial to the soil than monoculture. Conifers alone lead to acid conditions in the soil, but associated hardwoods are said to encourage the formation of microfungi which help the root hairs of conifers to absorb soil nutrients. A diversity of species also ensures that the belt is not of uniform height; an irregular profile and canopy break up the air-stream and reduce eddying. The best form for the belt is generally considered to be that of a house-roof, with a matrix of tall hardwoods at the centre and short, fast-growing, wind-firm conifers on the edges. A lower storey of shade-tolerant shrubs should also be included, to ensure that gaps do not develop in the lower layers of the belt as the trees grow. To ensure wind-firmness a belt should be reasonably dense; timber is then of better quality than that from a narrow belt.

In planting a shelterbelt, advantage should be taken of land-forms, such as ridges or spurs, which already provide a measure of protection; the saplings should be planted in the lee of these, so that they will establish themselves more rapidly and vigorously, as well as providing supplementary shelter. Hardy shrubs and small trees of indigenous species can be used as pioneers, to nurse the more slow-growing and sensitive species. Leguminous trees and shrubs are also commonly planted, so that their nitrogen-fixing nodules can enrich the soil and thus aid their neighbours. The development of a shelterbelt should in fact be treated as an ecological progression, while the completed belt, including the wild-life which will inevitably colonise it and much of which will perform biological control functions beneficial to the farm as a whole, can be regarded as a man-made ecological community.

In siting the belt a careful study must be made of the region's prevailing winds. Shelterbelts may be of many shapes; one which is favoured in British upland areas is a triple block of 'Manx-leg' form, which provides protection against winds blowing from any direction.

In clearing virgin bush on undulating ground, P. A. Yeomans of Sydney, Australia, originator of the well-known Keyline system of cultivation, advocates leaving shelterbelts of the indigenous trees on contour lines at approximately fifty-foot vertical intervals. Under Australian conditions, Yeomans reckons that the trees, when fully grown in the increasingly fertile soil which the Keyline system ensures, will provide almost complete wind protection to the entire area, as a line drawn from the top of one belt will touch the ground level of the next belt higher up. The system could of course be modified to suit conditions in any area, by adapting the intervals to the estimated maximum heights of the trees comprising the belts.

When new shelterbelts are created under the Keyline system, they are sited along lines parallel to the contour passing through the knickpoint – the geological term for the lowest point on a strip of undulating land where the gradient begins to flatten out and groundwater tends to gather, forming a spring. The reason for the choice of this layout is that the Keyline system provides for chisel-ploughing along those lines, as it has been found that this creates a multitude of narrow channels in the soil, which enables soil water to be spread out evenly and move freely, thus counteracting both waterlogging and desiccation, as well as erosion. This is the secret of the 'absorption fertility', which is the fundamental Keyline aim. Yeomans has proved incontrovertibly that the free circulation of mineral-laden groundwater, as well as radiation from the sun, oxygen and soil-organisms, for which his system provides, can lead to a rapid build-up of fertility, without any application of fertilisers or manures, simply by releasing the large quantities of soil nutrients which are normally locked up. On one of his farms, a foot of dark, friable topsoil was built up after only three years' Keyline treatment of land which had been so eroded, starved and compacted by bad husbandry that experts declared it incapable of restoration. In his latest book, *The City Forest*, Yeomans recommends the growing of trees and shrubs for stock fodder.

The planting of shelterbelts on livestock farms also aids the build-up of fertility, as animals tend to gather in their lees in bad weather, their droppings mingling with dead leaves, rich in minerals drawn from tree roots deep in the subsoil, to create a natural compost, the benefits of which gradually extend to a wide area of the surrounding land. On a forest farm, however, it is important to avoid over-stocking, as large quantities of animal manure can lead to excessive nitrogen, which tends to cause crop-bearing trees to grow timber at the expense of fruit.

Shelterbelts provide barriers against soil erosion by both wind and water, especially if 'brash' is left in windrows when bush is being cleared.

No part of the world would benefit more from the integration of agriculture with silviculture than the neglected uplands in many temperate areas of Europe and North America, such as Mid-Wales, the Pennine moors of Northern England, the Highlands of Scotland, the Auvergne in France and the abandoned farmlands of the Appalachians.

While many farms in Norway, Finland and the Alps include a forest component, British hill farmers in general seem unaware of the value of trees, though, in the days of 'high farming', the planting of shelterbelts was a recognised feature of upland development. Grid-shaped shelterbelts still existing in Scotland's southern uplands are memorials of reclamation schemes which formed part of the Agricultural Revolution of the eighteenth and early nineteenth century.

Trees, whether in the form of belts or blocks of woodland, can perform services of great economic value to the hill farmer. First and foremost, they provide protection against storm, wind and extremes of both heat and cold, without which neither livestock nor crops can really thrive. They thus lead to substantial economic benefits in the form of improved liveweight gains, increased milk and more abundant crops. In the case of sheep, shelter is especially important at lambing time and when a cold spell follows shearing. On upland pastures better strains of grass and clover can be sown, thus enabling cattle to be kept as well as sheep, and this mixed stocking leads in turn to pasture improvement. Protected pastures provide the 'early bite', which farmers greatly prize, as it enables economies to be made in corn feeding. Arable crops are less likely to be 'lodged' by wind or storm; it has been proved that far higher cereal yields can be obtained from tree-surrounded fields than from open, wind-swept prairies. In Russia increases of four hundred per cent have been recorded where wind-breaks have been provided for cereals.

Blocks of forest and shelterbelts are best sited on ground that is unsuitable for conventional cultivation, such as steep, rocky slopes or dingles. It is highly desirable to plant deep gullies with trees, otherwise they can become death-traps for sheep in blizzards. On sheep-walks a number of small blocks of woodland is preferable to long, linear belts, as these tend to interfere with the natural rhythms of the movement of sheep when grazing, known in Scotland as 'rakes'. Frost-pockets should be avoided when planting trees, as young saplings tend to be damaged by frost; also shelterbelts, copses or woods should not be sited below areas where it is intended to plant orchards or sow arable crops, as they hold up the downward flow of cold air and form frost-pockets on their upper sides.

Almost all trees require well drained soil. For this reason British foresters recommend the digging of open ditches above the site, though if Keyline ploughing or other methods of cultivation which improve soil structure are employed, ditches should not in general be needed. If ditches appear to be desirable, a second feature of the Keyline system could be introduced: a series a small reservoirs linked by open channels, which could be temporarily dammed and used for sheet irrigation in the event of drought. The reservoirs could be used for watering livestock, for ducks, for fish-culture and possibly for watercress beds. One of the aims of the Keyline system is to absorb all the rain that falls on a farm and make it 'work': the American Soil Conservation Service has demonstrated conclusively that a humus of good structure will absorb very large quantities of rain – even a tropical storm – without getting waterlogged or causing floods. Water that is absorbed and circulates freely in the soil is a valuable insurance against drought, whereas piped drainage removes water from where it is needed: under the crops. Also, it is useless to lay pipes beneath land where trees are to be planted, as they will be blocked and shattered by the trees' roots.

It is sometimes possible to plant trees in peat bogs without draining them. In Finland, where the practical uses of peat have been widely studied, nine types of bog have been classified as suitable for tree-planting, but only one, the 'herb-rich spruce bog', is considered capable of growing deciduous trees as well as conifers.

In Ireland bamboos have been grown on peat. The bamboo, which has many uses, including the production of asparagus-like edible shoots, is extremely quick-growing and can be harvested every five years. One Chinese bamboo, the moso, attains its full height of up to ninety feet in only a month and a half after the shoots break out of the earth – a growth rate of two feet a day.

For general purposes, there is a wide choice of trees for cool and temperate climates, such as that of the British Isles. Provided suitable types are selected trees may be established in almost any area. The choice of species should be governed by considerations of local soils – whether they are extremely acid, such as peat; or alkaline, as for example chalk and limestone. Then, the effects of atmospheric conditions must be kept in mind. Industrial pollution or close proximity to the seaside will influence the choice of particular tree species.

Species recommended by the British Forestry Commission for planting include :

ACID SOILS :

Birch	*Betula pendula*, silver birch; *B. pubescens*, brown birch, common on damp heaths; sub-species *odorata*, found in the Scottish Highlands; *B. nana*, the dwarf birch, a mountainous species of mid and north Scotland
Hornbeam	*Carpinus betulus*
Scots pine	*Pinus sylvestris*

NEUTRAL AND SLIGHTLY ACID SOILS :

Maple	*Acer platanoides*, Norway maple; *A. campestre*, common maple
Sycamore	*Acer pseudoplatanus*
Horse Chestnut	*Aesculus hippocastanum*
Birch	
Ash	*Fraxinus excelsior*
Hawthorns	*Crataegus laevigata*, two-styled hawthorn; *C. monogyna*, the common hawthorn; *C. media*, a hybrid type
Crab	*Malus sylvestris*, crab apple; *Malus domestica*, the cultivated apple, has also become naturalised as a wild species
Cherry	*Prunus laurocerasus*, cherry laurel; *P. mahaleb*; *P. serotina*, rum cherry; *P. avium*, gean or wild cherry; *P. padus*, the bird cherry Also various flowering cherries

Oak   *Quercus robur*, common oak; *Q. petraea*, sessile oak; *Q. rosacea*, a hybrid type; *Q. borealis*, the red oak or *Q. rubra*

Lime   *Tilia platyphyllos*, broad-leaved lime; *Tilia vulgaris*, common lime; *T. cordata*, the small-leaved lime, and hybrids of these species

SEASIDE:

Oak   *Quercus ilex*, Turkey oak; *Q. cerris*, evergreen or holm oak

Holly   *Eryngium maritimum*, sea holly; *Eryngium campestre*; *Ilex aquifolium*, holly

Pines   *Pinus nigra*, Austrian pine; *P. pinaster*, clustered pine; *P. radiata*
(*Picea abies*, the Norwegian spruce, and *Larix decidua*, the European larch, belong to the Pinaceae)

OPEN COUNTRYSIDE:

Oak, ash, horse chestnut, lime

DAMPER AREAS:

Alder   *Alnus glutinosa*, *Alnus incana*, often planted in Scotland. The berry-bearing alder is called *Frangula alnus*. It suits peaty heaths and damp hedges

Poplars   *Populus alba*, lobed or white poplar; *P. tremula*, aspen; *P. nigra*, black poplar; with sub-species *P. betulifolia* and *P. nigra × canadensis*, a hybrid, *P. serotina* and *P. italica*, the Lombardy poplar

Willows   *Salix pentandra*, bay willow; *S. triandra*, almond willow; *S. fragilis*, crack willow; *S. alba*, white willow; *S. purpurea*, purple willow; *S. viminalis*, common osier; *S. tapponum*, downy willow; *S. aurita*, eared willow; *S. caprea*, great sallow; *S. cinerea*, fen sallow, with sub-species *S. oleifolia*, common sallow and *S. atrocinerea*; *S. repens*, creeping willow; *S. nigricans*, dark-leaved willow; *S. phylicifolia*, tea-leaved willow; *S. hibernica*; *S. arbuscula*, little tree willow; *S. lanata*, woolly willow; *S. myrsinites*, myrtle-leaved willow; *S. herbacea*, least willow; *S. reticulata*, reticulate willow. The last eight species may be found on wet mountainous and rocky situations in the northern parts of Great Britain.

DOMESTIC GARDENS:

Where soils are rich, slightly acid and moist, maples, flowering crabs and cherries, birch, false acacia or *Robinia* species, including *R. pseudoacacia*, the American black locust tree, hawthorns, mountain ash or rowan (*Sorbus aucuparia*) are appropriate types to plant.

LARGER GARDENS, VILLAGES, OPEN SPACES AND NEW DEVELOPMENTS:
Cedar of Lebanon (*Cedrus libani*), Mt. Atlas Cedar (*C. atlantica*); and Deodar (*C. deodara*).
Beech (*Fagus sylvatica*) and other species; ash, lime, oaks, and false acacia

It is necessary to select sites for tree planting with care so that the mature trees will not interfere with drains, buildings and other facilities. Room for future development of the trees should be allowed. Do not plant trees when the land is waterlogged or frozen. The best times are normally during the months of November to March. In the case of less hardy species, planting in springtime is best. With deciduous types, it is most advisable to plant specimens after the leaves have fallen and before any buds come out. This avoids shock to the young seedlings or trees. Evergreens should be set out in late September or in late April or early May in cool climates. This information refers generally to seedling trees removed from the ground in nursery beds or self-seeded. Container-grown specimens, raised at home or bought from nurserymen and arboriculture establishments can be planted out at almost any period, except when it is frosty.

After planting out, water the trees as may be necessary, until they are established. It is vital to ensure that holes for tree planting are large enough to take the roots well spread out. A stake should be put in before positioning the young tree. The soil is then replaced in the hole and firmed down well around the plant. This can be done with the feet. Tie the tree firmly but not too tightly, and in proper upright position, to the stake. As it grows, loosen the tie to allow for increase in the girth until it is strong enough to stand alone and unaided. Never let the tie rub against the tree which it can do if it is too narrow or moves in the wind, so causing damage to the bark. The ground around the base of the stem should be kept free of weeds in a small circle until the tree is growing well. In dry weather a mulch of grass cuttings, leaf mould or similar material, should be put around the tree and watering given as required in the early stages for the first few months after planting or setting out.

Further interesting trees for general ornamental and environmental plantings include the larch (*Larix decidua*) suited to moist but well drained soils; the Scots pine (*Pinus sylvestris*) and the stone pine (*P. pinea*); the juniper (*Juniperus communis*); yew (*Taxus baccata*) the female trees of which should be kept away from livestock and children, owing to their poisonous berries; spindle tree or *Euonymus europaeus*; London plane or *Platanus × hybrida*; the elm (*Ulmus procera*), though this may be affected by endemic disease and falling branches often constitute a hazard; hazels or filberts (*Corylus* species); sweet or Spanish chestnut (*Castanea sativa*); and the strawberry tree or *Arbutus unedo*, found in southern England and South-West Ireland, as well as others.

A most valuable tree for the early stages of a shelterbelt is the Japanese larch, as it is one of the fastest growing trees in existence and can thus provide early shelter for stock, while its thinnings supply useful timber for fences and gates. Another fast-grower which is also highly wind-firm and resistant to pollution and a salt-laden atmosphere is Leyland's cypress. Still more hardy and suitable for the highest elevations and the poorest acid soils are lodgepole pine and mountain pine, while Sitka spruce is a vigorous tree which can provide quick shelter in regions of high rainfall. Much criticism has been aroused by the extensive growing of exotic conifers in the British uplands, and in fact conifer monoculture in regimented blocks is most undesirable, both from the aesthetic standpoint and because it leads to impoverishment of the soil. But conifers have vital functions to perform in areas where no other trees will grow and also as pioneers and nurses for hardwoods. However the tree which is most tolerant of adverse conditions in the British uplands is not a conifer but the rowan or mountain ash.

The rowan produces an edible berry, and no doubt a species could be bred which would fruit more prolifically. In Britain the possible role of shelterbelts as a source of food appears not to have been considered, but the Russians recommend pear trees and crab-apples as suitable for shelterbelts. Geans, or wild cherries, and hazels can also be planted, and there is no reason why black currants and cultivated blackberries should not be included in the shrub layers, provided that they are well fenced against stock. Philip Oyler, in his *Feeding Ourselves*, advocates the terracing of southern slopes for the growing of fruit trees, as is done in so many parts of Europe and Asia, and was commonly practised in England in earlier ages. The terracing of upland areas can be still seen from the 'strip lynchets', which survive in many areas. Terraces not only prevent erosion, but their walls conserve and reflect sunshine.

Oyler also suggests growing fruit trees in hedges. The potential of the traditional English hedgerow as a source of food for both human beings and livestock seems to have escaped most modern farmers, and yet such typical hedgerow plants as the elder, the hazel, the wild rose, the willow, the beech, the ash, the elm, the alder and the oak are rich in minerals and trace elements, which their deep roots draw from the subsoil, and are greedily browsed by animals, even in the depths of winter. Those farmers who have in recent years bulldozed thousands of miles of hedgerows, converting large areas of countryside into featureless, erosion-prone prairie, will surely come to realise that they have deprived themselves of a resource which could have gone a long way towards meeting the increased cost of imported feeding-stuffs.

Before the introduction of multiple-use forest farming schemes into upland regions of Europe and America, it would be necessary to carry out pioneer trials in selected areas. Plantings of economic species yielding forage and cereal substitutes could be made in already established plantations of conifers. The established species would provide ready-made shelter and act as guard trees for the exotic types. In due course, as the new trees developed, selective thinning of the conifers would commence, with grass and herbage seeding and appropriate stocking to produce fairly rapidly a forest-farm structure well adapted to multiple usage in terms of local needs.

In practice, any such scheme would best involve certain stages. First, the forested land would have to be chosen. This could contain various coniferous species, probably including some larch trees, pines and spruce, either in pure stands or planted as mixed species with other trees. An area of up to 500 acres would make a reasonable trial sector. During the initial year the forest should be thinned to provide a range of shelterbelts or breaks and suitable pasture conditions. This would give the forest farmer open glades of grass and herbage, some open woodland where the thinning of established species, such as larch, to about 500 specimens or stems per acre, would permit moderate sward development underneath the trees, and further relatively lightly thinned areas of additional species such as pines or spruce, which because of their dense coverage, might be expected to give valuable timber and satisfactory shelter for livestock grazing within the plantations. In the second year, grasses can be sown in the heavily thinned areas of the project as they are formed, choosing herbage species tolerant of shade where necessary. During the third year, the livestock could be introduced. Cattle and sheep would initially graze the undercover and ground herbage, thus stimulating new growth. Such grazing would expand on a regular basis when the land would be fully developed for forest farming, covering strips left for open pasture between the belts or blocks of the tree plantations.

Hill lands support pastures of such species as *Molinia caerulea* or the purple moor grass, which is common on fens and moors, and flowers in July to September, and *Nardus stricta* or mat grass also widespread on heaths, which flowers in June, July and August. One of the problems of land under such grasses is how to increase utilisation of pastures especially for sheep feeding. At present, the livestock can utilise little more than thirty per cent of the herbage, so low is its general quality. Nevertheless, these grasses do conserve the uplands and prevent erosion and offer a minimum sustenance to animals. But if supplemented and increased by the planting of suitable tree and shrub species of economic type which will yield appreciable quantities of cereal-substitutes and forage, the picture could be changed substantially for the better.

The native pasture species would continue to thrive under the canopies of the new trees and shrubs, and in due course it would become practicable to replace the indigenous grass species with better-quality grasses and clovers, including the deep-rooting herbs advocated by Elliott in the Clifton Park system which he pioneered in the Southern Uplands of Scotland. Pasture herbs such as chicory, burnet, sheep's parsley and birdsfoot trefoil are not only exceptionally rich in nutrients, but their roots penetrate to subsoil water and minerals; so that Elliott could report that, in times of drought, his fields were oases of green in a brown landscape.

Eventually the whole condition of many upland areas could be vastly improved by the practice of forest farming.

Useful species for growing in multiple usage farm schemes in Great Britain would include :

SPECIES	PRODUCTS AND USE	REMARKS
Caragana arborescens (Siberian peatree)	Small pods or beans	Very hardy shrub, thrives in Manitoba
Castanea species (Sweet chestnut)	Nuts for meal	Four economic species, including the Japanese and Chinese chestnuts which may withstand greater cold than the European type. Improved blight-resistant strains are superior
Corylus species (Hazelnut)	Nuts for meal	Suitable for secondary layers under fairly open upper canopies of taller species. There are eleven useful species, of which at least half a dozen will thrive in cold regions
Crataegus species (Hawthorn)	Dried fruits for grinding into meal. Fodder	Numerous species, many resistant to cold. Proper selection of thornless types is desirable
Fagus species (Beech)	Nuts or 'mast'	Both European and American species are hardy. The mast was formerly a staple food for village livestock but yearly production is variable
Gleditsia triacanthos (Honey locust)	Pods for meal	Rich in sugar. The species is tolerant of frost, flourishing in New York State

SPECIES	PRODUCTS AND USE	REMARKS
Juglans species (Walnuts)	Nuts for grinding into meal	There are some eighteen economic species, of which several thrive in cold temperate regions. Grafted, high-yielding, quick growing planting material should be used
Pinus species (Pinenut)	Nuts for meal	Eighteen species are known to produce edible nuts. Many are tolerant of severe cold. The stone pine was grown in the British Isles by the Romans for animal and human food
Prunus amygdalus (Almond)	Nuts for meal	Many varieties. Needs protection from wind in exposed sites by guard trees. Rich in calcium
Quercus species (Oak)	Acorns for grinding into meal	Several useful species. Furnish important food for wild-life, but bearing often slower and perhaps irregular

It is essential to select improved strains which bear quickly and give higher yields. These are now becoming increasingly available from plant breeding stations in several countries.

12

Fields for Expansion
ii. Deserts

'Les forêts précedent les civilisations, les déserts les suivent' – CHATEAUBRIAND

NEARLY ONE THIRD of the earth's land surface is desert. The evidence of abandoned cities, choked wells and cisterns, rock paintings and ancient records proves that large areas were once fertile and populous. One of the supreme challenges of the twentieth and twenty-first centuries must be to find ways of regenerating a considerable proportion of the world's deserts so that they may again support human beings under decent living conditions, and thus ease the pressure on the cities and other densely inhabited regions caused by the population explosion.

In recent decades important schemes of desert reclamation and research have been carried out in several countries, notably the North African states, Israel, the South-West United States and China. China reclaimed nearly two million acres of desert in about twenty years. These achievements demonstrate conclusively that, by a combination of modern and traditional techniques, it is possible to carry farming and horticulture to desert areas on a large scale.

In dealing with the crucial problem of water four main approaches have been evolved:

1. conveying water by canal or pipe from the nearest river, lake or mountain range;

2. tapping underground sources by sinking wells or boreholes;

3. catching rain by means of bunds or cisterns;

4. planting drought-resistant bushes or trees.

Generally a balanced combination of at least three of these methods has been employed where projects have been successful. Increasing emphasis is being laid on the importance of finding the most suitable varieties of trees and shrubs which shall perform the multiple functions of stabilising the soil; tapping and controlling any underground water that may be available; attracting precipitation and causing its absorption into the ground; retarding evaporation, and providing nurse conditions for more sensitive economic crops; while also supplying food, fodder, fuel, timber and possibly other products. Once tree belts have been established, including forage species, it is possible to consider the introduction of hardy livestock, and irrigation channels are sometimes stocked with fish. In order to gain the fullest benefit from all factors in the environment, a scientifically planned desert-reclamation project should involve multi-use resource development on forest-farming lines.

One of the great advantages of making tree-planting the spearhead of desert reclamation is that trees, especially of drought-resistant species, are less dependent on water than annual crops; and this reduces the need for expensive irrigation schemes, which often involve the construction of large dams drowning thousands of acres of land and lead to alkalisation problems. Trees seek out their own water supplies, sending their roots sometimes hundreds of feet into the subsoil, and creating their own local irrigation systems, which benefit their shallow-rooting neighbours as well as themselves, and which, being underground, are not subject to evaporation, whereas, especially in tropical climates, at least half the water trapped behind a big dam may be evaporated.

For supplying the modest moisture requirements of young trees before their roots tap sufficient subsoil sources, various devices have been employed. In Algeria a system known as *potet masqué* has been evolved.

A rim of topsoil is removed round the seedling, which is then surrounded by dried vegetation, cut for the purpose in the spring, and stones are placed on top. Two litres only of water are applied when planting; the mulch of vegetation acts as a sponge for retaining the moisture and the stones impede evaporation. (A somewhat similar system known as 'box-bunding' has been applied to

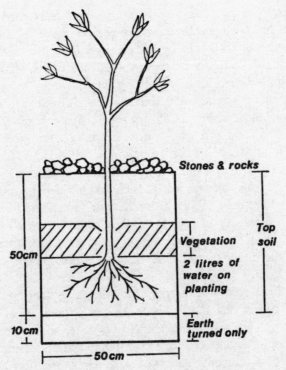

Fig 16. Potet Masqué system of planting

tung oil trees in Malawi. Each tree was planted in a rectangular basin in which litter from the trees was accumulated and rotted down, forming a natural compost and absorbing rainfall and dew.) In undulating areas, contour ditches or slightly sloping terraces, known in Algeria as *banquettes* (see p. 50), can be constructed to collect and distribute to trees any rain that may fall; while the system could be made still more effective by the method employed in rubber plantations of digging silt-pits close to each tree, to trap the fine soil carried by the water. Bunds, or small earth dams, are commonly constructed to trap rain falling into wadis or depressions, the water then being conveyed to cultivated areas by leats. A practice followed by Berbers on a limestone plateau in Tunisia was to build dry-stone dams across erosion gullies, and plant olive trees in the silt which piled up behind the dams.

Important research into 'run-off agriculture' has been carried out by Prof. Michael Evenari, of the Hebrew University, Jerusalem, in an area of minimal rainfall of the Negev, south Israel. Copying methods employed by the Nabateans nearly 2,000 years ago, Evenari has succeeded in growing thousands of nut and fruit trees and fodder shrubs in an area that sometimes receives no rain for eleven months. The methods he employs includes the construction of bunds (which he calls *limanes*), of contour catchments, and of microcatchments, which are small rain-collecting areas, each one serving only a single tree. His system has been so successful that it is being adopted on a much larger scale under the auspices of a German relief organisation in Afghanistan. For livestock Evenari has employed the very hardy Awassi sheep which are capable of surviving under desert conditions.

A problem affecting certain arid areas is that water supplies, both subterranean and on the surface, may be high in salinity. Recent work undertaken in several regions has shown that, in certain circumstances, it is possible to employ salt waters, even with a T.D.S. (total dilution of solids) as much as that of sea water.[1] At present, the employment of highly saline water for irrigation is confined to sandy soils, where there is good drainage. Much research has been done into the subject at the Negev Institute for Arid Zone Research in Israel, where there are large supplies of brackish waters underground, notably in a semi-artesian aquifer some 500 metres below the western Negev desert. Investigators are exploring two solutions to the problem: the development of economical desalination processes and agricultural techniques permitting the use of untreated brackish water for irrigation. Three desalination techniques have so far been investigated: reverse osmosis, electrodialysis and ion exchange, and a number of pilot plants have been constructed. Much work has also been done in Israel into techniques for re-cycling industrial and municipal water. The use of brackish water for irrigation must involve methods that avoid the build-up of salinity in the soil, and also finding or breeding salt-resistant plants.

A simple method for growing plants, including trees, in arid

[1] *Saline irrigation for agriculture and forestry.* U.N.E.S.C.O./W.A.A.S. Italy Symposium, edited by H. Boyko (W.A.A.S. series, World Academy of Art and Science, Vol. IV., pp. xii, 350, W. Junk, The Hague, 1968).

areas with salinity problems has been developed by the Central Soil Salinity Research Institute at Karnal, India. It involves sinking baked porous earthen pitchers, about twelve inches in diameter, in pits filled with soil and manure, and planting the trees close to the pitchers, which are filled with water by hand every day. Research indicates that this method, which is very suitable for areas where there are no agricultural labour problems, involves far less water than conventional irrigation systems. The water issuing from the porous walls of the pitchers should displace salt in the immediate neighbourhood of each plant, therefore desalination techniques entailing the soaking of an entire area, which is very wasteful of water, can be dispensed with.

The location of underground watercourses in arid areas can often be discovered by studying aerial photographs for the lines along which surviving indigenous vegetation is growing.

For the stabilisation of dunes, so that trees and bushes can be successfully established, spraying with petrol or emulsions has been found a satisfactory solution in north Africa. In Chinese deserts, shifting sands are covered with grids made by hand of soil, weeds, tree branches and pebbles, saplings being planted in the middle of each square. The trees which have been found most suitable for stabilising dunes in the Negev and North Africa have been the tamarisk, which can withstand very severe droughts, and various species of acacia and eucalyptus, which rapidly send out deep roots to tap the groundwater. It is important to remember, however, that the eucalyptus requires large quantities of water – it has been estimated that a single tree can transpire eighty gallons in a day. Eucalyptus plantations have been employed on a large scale in Israel for the reclamation of swamps. Therefore it is important to avoid using eucalyptus in areas where groundwater supplies are known to be limited, otherwise the risk exists that they will cause wells and springs to dry up.

Sometimes, if all grazing is prohibited in an arid area being reclaimed, there will be sufficient regeneration of the natural grasses and other vegetation to stabilise the sands. The wild species can then be used as nurse crops for economic trees.

In some parts of the Negev and north Africa it has been found possible to plant trees without any watering on earth ridges, as the loose earth conserves moisture, allows the free circulation of oxygen and minerals, and thus encourages the trees to mesh out rapidly into a well developed root system. However a new system of watering called 'pulsed irrigation', devised by Dr Benjamin Zur, of Technion, the Israel Institute of Technology, can give the most efficient results with a low expenditure of water.

Probably the most widely used tree for the early stages of desert reclamation projects is the acacia, many species of which are highly drought-resistant. In a project sponsored by Oxfam designed to halt the advance of the Sahara in the Niger area of the Sahel zone, large quantities of acacia seeds have been sown, some encased in the droppings of goats which had browsed on acacia bushes. The goat, whose uncontrolled grazing has been one of the main causes of the spread of desert conditions, was thus being used to help the process of regeneration by means of its manure.

Two other trees that will stand highly arid conditions are the olive and carob, though Prof. Evenari has found that, for the purposes of his desert 'run-off' scheme, the most efficient trees have been almonds and pistachios. Prof. Evenari has also successfully grown apples, peaches, apricots, vines and boysenberries, while Wendy Campbell-Purdie, in her desert reclamation scheme at Bou Saada in Algeria, succeeded in establishing citrus trees, figs, pomegranates and honey locusts. In China many orchards have been planted in desert areas following pioneer plantings of drought-resistant shrubs, such as the sand sagebush and the sand willow, and of shelterbelts of trees which, in more temperate zones, include poplars, birches, elms and cypresses. In the Gobi desert large plantations of Chinese dates have been established.

Date palms are, of course, a feature of many oases in the Sahara and the Middle East. In Tunis, oases exist where dates are believed to have been grown continuously since Roman times. The tall date-palm is well suited to a two-storey or three-storey system, as low trees, such as olives, apricots, figs and citrus varieties, can grow beneath it, with beans and other leguminous crops on the ground level, to inject nitrogen into the soil for the benefit of the entire plant community. By this type of ecological cultivation, a very high degree of productivity can be achieved, even in arid areas. Tall-growing trees with open canopies suitable for the top storey of multi-storey systems in *non*-arid areas include the walnut and pecan.

Other food-producing trees which will withstand arid conditions include the persimmon and nut-bearing pines, of which large numbers grow on otherwise barren hillsides in New Mexico.

The Negev Institute for Arid Zone Research has experimented with hundreds of types of perennial bushes which have proved their value for fodder production. Many species have been imported from Australia, which, as a relatively new continent, has not undergone the history of overgrazing which has impoverished desert vegetation in Asia and Africa, and therefore offers a wide selection of drought-resistant fodder bushes. After experimental plantings in the institute's nurseries, the most successful species, which included salt bushes and blue bush acacias, were planted in larger plots in various parts of the Negev, and, following a further period, during which improved species were bred, a big plantation was established in the Beersheba area, where rainfall rarely exceeds eight inches a year. Though no irrigation was applied, this plantation grew into what has been described as a 'verdant jungle', which was grazed by both sheep and cattle. The animals throve on the drought fodder, needing no additional feeds. Desert soils are often very rich in minerals, so that any crops that can be established in them are often of outstanding quality and nutritional value.

This has been amply demonstrated, according to St Barbe Baker, in the desert-colonisation schemes inaugurated in Egypt under Colonel Nasser. In the Tahrir province, for example, first-class vegetables are grown in orange groves on five-acre holdings distributed to colonists and irrigated by channels from the Nile, stocked with edible fish.

Multiple land-use techniques, including widespread tree planting on forest-farming lines, would not only alleviate the problems of food shortages in many stricken areas, but would also help to conserve natural resources and provide pleasant and stimulating environments, thus contributing to a reversal of the present drift of rural populations to the towns.

Three-dimensional forestry is the antithesis of destructive one-crop farming or the planting of single-type trees, which being monocultures, have to be isolated from natural factors. On the contrary, forest farming aims to create ecologically balanced complexes, working in harmony with Nature, but capable of profitable returns. For this reason, the methods are fully compatible with the principles and practice of conservation and the protection of wild-life. Those who presently oppose or dislike nature reserves will have much of the ground cut away from under their feet when it becomes general knowledge that here is a way of integrating economic results with the preservation and indeed improvement of the countryside. Not only can three-dimensional forestry makes possible the conduct of agri-silvicultural operations inside nature reserves, without damaging their essential purposes, but it can also open up new avenues of employment and land usage, offering a means of developing immense acreages of marginal ground, now lying neglected and providing a powerful counter-attraction to the menace of persistent industrialisation and the evils of spreading megalopoli cut off from the life of the soil.

In these days of widespread pollution, trees can perform a valuable service in purifying the atmosphere of regions close to industrial conurbations. Trees that are especially helpful in this respect are the honey locust, certain species of pine (the Black Forest in Germany is known for its salubrious atmosphere) and the balsam poplar, whose delicious scent, under favourable wind conditions, can be wafted over a wide area. Tree planting, especially for stabilisation purposes on river banks, could also do much to prevent the floods that cause devastation in many parts of the world.

Forest-farming schemes would offer favourable conditions for the alternative-technology devices, which cause minimal pollution and depletion of non-renewable resources. For example, in creating a shelterbelt system, it would be possible to leave a gap within a belt or between two belts, lined with exceptionally wind-firm trees and facing in the direction of the prevailing wind. This would have the effect of funnelling and therefore greatly intensifying the strength of the wind; and the leeward end would be a suitable site for an electricity-generating or pumping windmill. If small dams are built in connection with irrigation schemes, waterwheels could be inserted, for the generation of electric power or for forage-grinding mills. In Israel, desert outposts are provided with small one-kilowatt turbo-generators powered by solar energy, capable of providing light for twenty-six families and irrigation for eight acres of farmland. Solar heating devices could also be constructed for homes and greenhouses, and the dung of housed livestock could be converted into methane gas for heating and power.

These are a few examples of the technical installations that could be built into a forest-farming scheme. Others are: sawmills, papermills, canning factories, animal-feedingstuff plants, factories for the processing of fibres, gums, oils and other forest products, furniture factories, and cooperative workshops for the manufacture and maintaining of farm machinery, especially machinery of the intermediate-technology type, suitable for decentralised communities in relatively undeveloped areas (see literature of Intermediate Technology Publications Ltd, 9 King Street, London WC2E 8HN, England).

Forest farming itself involves a number of skilled tasks, such as pruning, grafting and the breeding of improved species of trees and livestock, while there is room for specialised research institutes to investigate the many avenues for development which the 3D concept opens up, especially the ecological relationships between various trees and other plants. For example, it is known that if plum-trees are interplanted with blackcurrants, the association is mutually beneficial, but the scientific reason for its efficacy and for that of many other multiple-cropping systems found in traditional husbandry has never been investigated.

By the development of forest-farming projects, both on a small and a large scale, incorporating ecological and conservationist techniques, it would be possible greatly to increase the productivity of almost any area where trees will grow. Numerous opportunities could be opened up for the self-sufficiency schemes which are arousing so much interest today; families could subsist, providing all their own essential needs of food, fuel, clothing and shelter without excessive expenditure of labour, on very small plots, from, say, two acres upwards.

Within a forest-farming complex, new rural communities could be established, catering for all the physical and cultural needs of mankind, and involving skills of all kinds which would give their inhabitants status fully comparable with that of urban workers. This might well prove a powerful attraction to the technically minded young men and women of today, reversing the drift to the towns, solving unemployment problems and countering all the undesirable effects of excessive urbanisation.

Another great attraction of such schemes would be the opportunities of attaining far higher degrees of health than are available to towndwellers. The products of a forest farm are capable of providing all the nutritional needs of both human beings and animals, and the inhabitants of communities, subsisting on fresh, locally grown produce, in unpolluted surroundings, might well enjoy levels of positive health which are seldom known today. Tree-products are especially rich in the minerals and vitamins in which so many diets of both town-dwellers and country people are deficient.

Civilisations have been born out of the immense fertility and wide power of satisfying human needs provided by forest conditions. Later the same civilisations have succumbed to the devastation and erosion caused by excessive and uncontrolled tree-felling, without provision for natural regeneration, and the sites of many ancient cities are now uninhabited deserts. Out of a widespread movement for the establishment of forest farms in many parts of the world, it is possible to envisage the establishment of new ecologically based civilisations, more vital and more profoundly satisfying to all man's deepest needs than any known before.

The table overleaf lists the average food values of a number of important tree products.

COMPOSITION AND NUTRITIVE VALUE OF SOME FEEDING STUFFS
PRODUCED BY TREE CROPS

ITEM	Protein (g)	Carbo-hydrate (g)	Fat (g)	Calcium (mg)	Iron (mg)	Vitamin A (IU)	B₁ (mg)	B₂ (mg)	Niacin (mg)	Vitamin C (mg)
African locust beans (Parkia spp)	26.0	50.0	10.0	90.0	6.3	—	0.06	0.20	3.0	trace
Algaroba pods (Prosopis spp)	17.0	65.0	2.0	260.0	4.0	—	—	—	—	—
Almonds (Prunus amygdalus)	18.6	19.5	54.2	234.0	4.7	—	0.24	0.92	3.5	—
Brazil-nuts (Bertholletia excelsa)	14.3	10.9	66.9	186.0	3.4	trace	0.96	0.12	1.6	trace
Breadfruit (Artocarpus incisa)	1.3	21.5	0.3	28.0	0.5	20	0.09	0.06	0.8	22.0
Carob beans (Ceratonia siliqua)	21.0	66.0	1.5	130.0	3.8	—	—	—	—	—
Cashew-nuts (Anacardium occidentale)	17.2	29.3	45.7	38.0	3.8	100	0.43	0.25	1.8	—
Cassava leaves	6.8	9.6	1.1	175.0	1.7	10000	0.16	0.30	1.8	265.0
Cassava meal and flour (Manihot utilissima and M. palmata)	1.5	60.5	0.6	12.0	1.0	trace	—	—	1.0	—
Chestnuts (Castanea spp)	6.7	78.0	4.1	53.0	3.4	—	0.32	0.38	1.2	—
Coconut meat (Cocos nucifera)	3.5	9.4	35.0	13.0	1.7	—	0.5	0.2	0.5	—
Dates (Phoenix dactylifera)	2.5	73.0	0.6	73.0	2.7	80	0.12	0.11	1.6	trace
Hazel-nuts or filberts (Corylus spp)	12.8	17.0	62.0	210.0	3.5	trace	0.46	0.25	0.9	—

Hickorynuts or pecans (Carya spp)	9.4	15.0	71.0	74.0	2.5	130	0.86	0.13	0.9	—
Honeylocust pods (Gleditsia triacanthos)	16.0	60.5	7.5	200	3.8	—	—	—	—	—
Jack-fruit (Artocarpus integrifolia)	0.4	21.8	0.2	8.0	0.2	490	0.05	0.03	0.4	3.0
Olives (Olea europea)	1.5	—	24.0	58.0	2.6	200	0.03	0.24	1.0	—
Palm kernel cake (Elaeis guineenis)	19.0	73.0	6.0	—	—	—	—	—	—	—
Persimmons (Diospyros spp)	0.6	20.0	0.2	7.0	0.4	1900	0.05	0.05	trace	9.0
Pignolias	31.0	13.0	47.5	11.0	4.5	—	0.62	—	—	—
Pinons (Pinus spp)	14.0	20.5	60.0	12.0	5.2	30	1.28	0.23	4.5	—
Pistachios (Pistacia vera)	16.0	18.0	58.0	100.0	3.0	trace	0.32	0.25	1.5	trace
Walnuts (Juglans species)	16.0	15.5	64.0	99.0	3.2	30	0.33	0.13	0.9	—
West Indian cherry (Malpighia spp)	1.6	13.7	0.1	16.0	8.0	30	0.02	0.04	0.5	1000.0

Note: The figures given are average ones, and variations occur according to the locality of growth and the strain or cultivar. Food composition per 100g dry matter.

Sources:

Food and Agricultural Organisation of the United Nations (F.A.O), *Food Composition Tables for International Use,* Rome, 1949.

F.A.O, *Food Composition Tables – Minerals and Vitamins – for International Use,* Rome, 1954.

United Kingdom Medical Research Council, *Tables of Representative Values of Foods Commonly Used in Tropical Countries,* rev. ed., B. S. Platt, London, 1962.

Institute of Nutrition of Central America and Panama – Interdepartmental Committee on Nutrition for National Defense, *Food Composition Tables for Use in Latin America,* Washington, D.C., 1961.

Appendix I
Ancillary Species for Fodder, Conservation and Other Purposes

APART FROM the main task of tree-cropping programmes, which is to produce foodstuffs for use as cereal-substitutes and for manufacturing, ancillary developments also assist in raising total output. In helping to achieve a varied and satisfactory series of harvests and products, the species listed in this Appendix perform many useful functions in addition to that of yielding crops, including making available green manures, checking erosion, ensuring land conservation, bearing flowers and blossoms for honey-gathering bees, providing timber, fuel, firewood, charcoal, in some cases gum, resins, and similar items, as well as fruits, fibres and materials of all kinds, both for farm maintenance and use and for sale. In short, selections have been made, generally speaking, with the object of choosing species that have multiple uses. Many other plants do offer services in land conservation and reclamation or yield crops, but often their scope is limited to a single product. Therefore it is better to ignore such species and concentrate on the more versatile types.

There are numerous browse plants and other miscellaneous products of vegetation[1] which can provide useful sources of sup-

---

[1] Botanical names of noted species not given in the text are:

Cabbage broccoli	hybrid between *Brassica oleracea*, var., and *Brassica oleracea botrytis*
Soya beans	*Glycine hispida*
Sulla clover	*Hedysarum coronarium* (also called Spanish sanfoin)
Alfalfa or lucerne	*Medicago sativa*. Numerous varieties and strains
Lyon bean	*Mucuna deeringianum*
Berseem	*Trifolium alexandrinum*
Prickly pears	*Opuntia dillenii*
Sisal	*Agave sisalana* and *Agave fourcroydes*
Rubber	*Hevea* species

plementary green food for eating fresh or making into hay and silage on forest farms. Outstanding species of this type include *Desmodium gyrans*, an erect leguminous perennial, enjoyed by cattle; cabbage broccoli or kale; certain varieties of soya beans; sulla clover which yields up to as much as fifty tons per acre and is widely valued; alfalfa or lucerne, where some irrigation is available in dry regions; the lyon bean, an excellent source of fodder; and berseem, well known throughout the Middle East, which thrives on saline land. Prickly pears are good, too, but are best ensiled, the succulent spiny growths if present being well crushed and flavoured with salt or mixed with other fodder before putting into pits. The silage so prepared is very fattening. The spineless forms are superior for cultivation. The foliage and flowers of the common elders (*Sambucus nigra* et al.,) the berries of which are used for wine-making and the leaves as substitutes for spinach, also form good livestock fodder. The by-products of sisal plantations, the leaves of rubber trees, gorse (*Ulex* spp.), tea-bush cuttings, and palm fronds, to mention only a few lesser known items, can all, after processing, be employed for the efficient feeding of farm animals as supplementary rations and roughage. Species such as *Fraxinus ornus*, some *Tamarix* spp., certain *Erythrinas* and some types of *Polygonum* also yield useful products. With the exercise of a little ingenuity, a number of indigenous, but currently neglected local plants may often be turned to good account and commercial exploitation. These can help out at different seasons with benefit.

Various *Acacia* spp., including *A. baileyana*, *A. cyanophylla*, *A. arabica*, and *A. melanoxylon*, are very satisfactory for poor soils or sandy localities. Valuable legumes, like hairy vetch (*Vicia villosa*); clovers; and lucernes; as well as nurse plants such as oats, sesame, barley, rye, and Sudan grass also have useful parts to play for fodder production on open strips. For green manuring, *Adhatoda vasica*; *Aleurites triloba*; *Azadirachta indica* or margosa; *Croton lacciferus*; *Erythrina lithosperma*; *Gliricidia maculata* or madera; *Grevillea robusta*, the silky oak; *Inga laurina* or Spanish ash; *Myroxylon toluifera*; *Tecoma leucoxylon*, also called white cedar; and *Tithonia diversifolia*, the Mexican sunflower, are important, while some of these species additionally make good windbreak types. Foresters and farmers should also bear in mind the usefulness of various *Albizzia* spp.; different hedge plants for barriers, boundaries, and the safeguarding of *banquettes* or ditches; *Salix alba* or the golden willow, for holding up the banks of gullies; *Amorpha fructicosa*, or bastard indigo; sisal; safflower; castor bean plants; figs, poplars; many *Eucalyptus* spp.; *Panicum antidotale*; *Cenchrus ciliaris*; osage oranges; Russian mulberry; comfrey; and other types. These notes are not exhaustive, and reference should be made to detailed literature when choosing species for different soils and climates. Many new hybrids, strains, and cultivars have been produced, which give superior results, and whenever possible such planting material should be used in preference to unimproved lots.

Amarantus spp., including especially *A. frumentaceus*, *A. gangeticus*, *A. melancholicus*, *A. oleraceus*, *A. paniculatus*, and *A. tricolor*, yield both green foliage and edible seeds, which can be ground into meal. There is scope for the planting of catch crops, like cassava (*Manihot utilissima*) of the sweet varieties; or fruiting bamboos (*Melocanna bambusoides*), which bear fleshy fruits and have edible pericarps; and the culture of numerous kinds of vegetables, small fruits, edible flowers, root crops and other products in forest farms, particularly before trees attain enough height to occupy the ground completely. In addition, several different sorts of cash crops which give quick returns may be employed to bring in temporary income. *Trapa bicornis*, or the water chestnut, belonging to the family Onagraceae, can be cultivated on dams or stretches of still water for its nuts, which make excellent and nutritious livestock feed after milling. Perusal of appropriate literature on economic botany will enable readers to discover many more suitable ancillary species of productive value, at present little known amongst farmers and foresters.

The following species are also worthy of consideration, after trial in new localities:

NAME	FOOD PRODUCT
Acalypha indica	Leaves for fodder
Achyranthes aspera	Leaves for fodder
Acrostichum aureum	Fronds for fodder
Aerva lanata	Stems and leaves for fodder

NAME	FOOD PRODUCT
Allmania nodiflora	Leaves for fodder
Alternanthera triandra	Leaves and stems for fodder
Argyeia populifolia	Leaves for fodder
Asparagus falcatus	Shoots for feeding
Asplenium esculentum	Fronds for fodder
Astragalus sinicus	Legume for wet land
Boerhaavia diffusa	Leaves for fodder
Cassia auriculata	Pods, leaves and flowers for fodder
Cassia occidentalis	Pods, leaves and flowers for fodder
Cassia tomentosa	Pods, leaves and flowers for fodder
Cassia tora	Pods, leaves and flowers for fodder
Celosia argentea	Stems and leaves for fodder
Ceratopteris thalictroides	Fronds for fodder
Cicer arietinum	Legume (Chickpea)
Commelina clavata	Stems and leaves for fodder
Dregia volubilis	Leaves for fodder
Hibiscus furcatus	Leaves for fodder
Hydrocotyle asiatica	Stalks and leaves for fodder
Impatiens flaccida	Stems and leaves for fodder
Klugia notoniana	Leaves for fodder
Lasia spinosa	Leaves for fodder
Leucas zeylanica	Leaves for fodder
Lippia nudiflora	Leaves for fodder
Lupinus species	Mostly *L. alba* for fodder
Marsilea quadrifolia	Stalks and leaves for fodder
Monochoria hastaefolia	Stalks and leaves for fodder
Nasturtium officinale	Stalks and leaves for fodder
	Also useful for grazing
*Nelumbium speciosum**	Edible seeds
*Nymphaea lotus**	Edible seeds
Oxalis corniculata	Stalks and leaves for fodder
Phaseolus species	Beans of various kinds
Portulaca oleracea	Edible stems and leaves; grazing
Portulaca quadrifida	Edible stems and leaves; grazing
Portulaca tuberosa	Edible stems and leaves; grazing
Psophocarpus tetragonolobus	Bean
Psoralea species	Grazing and fodder
Solanum indicum	Fruits and leaves for fodder
Solanum nigrum	Fruits and leaves for fodder
Solanum xanthocarpum	Fruits and leaves for fodder
Stizolobium deeringianum	Bean
Typhonium trilobatum	Leaves for fodder
Vicia species	Vetch
Vigna sinensis	Cowpea

* Grows in water, suitable for tanks or small lakes, where waterfowl are kept.

There is a perennial bush form of the sword bean (*Canavalia ensiformis*) which can be grown under young trees. The plants yield both green forage and pods with beans. *Centrosema plumieri*, the butterfly pea, also forms a good ground cover under newly planted blocks or belts, or in open strips, and cattle or other livestock relish the cuttings of foliage. Another species is *Centrosema pubescens*, with similar value. *Pueraria thunbergiana*, a herbaceous creeper, is much cultivated as partial food crop in China and Japan, the leaves and shoots being edible, while the roots yield starch and the stems a satisfactory fibre. *Musa* species can also be planted, if the conditions are suitable.

FURTHER SPECIES

LEGUMES

NAME	REMARKS
Amorpha canescens (lead plant)	Drought-resistant, good in pastures
Cajanus indicus (pigeon pea)	Drought-resistant, can be sown in pasturage
Cajanus species	Drought resistant
Cyamopsis tetragonoloba (cluster bean)	Fodder
Desmanthus virgatus	Pastures, hardy, prefers moist conditions
Desmodium discolor (horse marmalade)	Excellent browse; sub-tropical or summertime in cold areas
Desmodium asperum	Excellent browse
Desmodium pabularis	Excellent browse
Desmodium heterophyllum	Herb, suited to warm and moist areas
Desmodium triflorum	Drought-resisting, with small clover-like leaves
Desmodium uncinatum	Browse
Desmodium wrightii	Browse
Dolichos biflorus	Creeping habit, drought-resistant; fodder
Glycine javanica	Pasture legume
Hedysarum coronarium (Spanish sainfoin)	Likes deep moist soils, high-yielding herb
Indigophera arrecta	Browse; hardy
Indigophera spicata	Pasture bush
Lespedeza sericea	Drought-resistant, pasture plant; perennial species
Lespedeza stipulacea	Drought-resistant; grows on poor soils; fodder; annual type

NAME	REMARKS
Lotus corniculatus (Bird's-foot trefoil)	Adaptable, can grow under wet or dry conditions. Prefers cool areas; fodder or pastures
Lotus uliginosus	Adaptable
Medicago orbiculari (button clover)	Annual
Medicago tribuloides (barrel clover)	Frost-resistant; grows under dry conditions on alkaline soils
Melilotus alba (Bokhara clover)	Good for renovation, biennial
Onobrychis viciifolia (sainfoin)	Likes chalky soils, resists drought, dislikes waterlogging; pastures
Ornithopus sativus (serradella)	Annual, reseeding itself; fodder plant
Pachyrhizus tuberosus	Vigorous grower; fodder
Petalostemon candidum (prairie clover)	Pasture legume
Petalostemon purpureum	Pasture legume
Pueraria thunbergiana (kudzu)	Fodder; needs good soils and moisture
Trifolium hirtum (rose clover)	Grows on thin dry soils; fodder; good coloniser
Trifolium subterraneum (subterranean clover)	Drought-resistant; annual but self-seeding; fodder, pastures, grows on poorer land

FORAGE AND FODDER

NAME	REMARKS
Carpobrotus edulis	A creeping succulent; good on sand and colonising bare land; forage
Cichorium intybus (chicory)	Drought resistant, deep-rooted herb; grows on poor soils; fodder, can be mixed with legumes and grasses
Cryophytum crystallinum	Creeping succulent
Mesembryanthemum species	Hardy and succulent; fodder
Mikania scandens (mile-a-minute)	Hardy, but prefers moister conditions; excellent livestock forage; not suitable for conventional farms, as it can spread rapidly and become a weed, but satisfactory in agri-silviculture
Portulacaria afra (elephant food)	Succulent, drought-resistant; fodder; tolerant of frost
Phoenix dactylifera (date palm)	Fruits for drying; commonly fed to stock in desert areas

Perennial clovers are most useful, but will not stand hot and dry conditions.

CEREALS, DRY GRAINS, AND SIMILAR PLANTS FOR FODDER

NAME	REMARKS
Chenopodium album (bajar)	Suits warm areas; foliage and seeds similar to buckwheat
Chenopodium quinoa (quinoa)	Small seeds, must be soaked before milling into meal to remove bitter properties
Eleusine coracana (ragi)	Suits variable soils in dry climates; seeds for grinding into meal
Fagopyrum esculentum (buckwheat)	Grows on poor soils; seeds can be milled into meal
Panicum miliaceum (Indian millet)	Yields grass crops or grain
Panicum miliare (little millet)	Annual grass, as well as grains
Setaria italica (Italian millet)	Annual grass; grains very nutritious and digestible

Avena spp., both wild and cultivated; *Triticum vulgare*; *Zea mays*; dryland rice species (*Oryza sativa*); barley species (*Hordeum* types); and *Secale cereale* all make good forage crops in suitable areas. There are also numerous uncultivated relatives of these cereal grasses, with value for grazing purposes or fodder. *Agropyrum junceum* is another potentially significant species. It can be hybridised with wheat and grows in saline or sandy soils.

DROUGHT FODDER

ALGAROBAS : *Prosopsis africana, P. alba, P. blanca, P. caldenia, P. chilensis, P. cineraria, P. fareta, P. glandulosa, P. stephaniana, P. tamarugo.*

ACACIAS : *Acacia excelsa, A. harpophylla, A. albida, A. aneura, A. brachystachya.*

VARIOUS : *Cytisus scoparius, Ventilago viminalis, Pittosporum phillyraeoides, Owenia acidula, Myoporum platycarpum, Heterodendrum deaefolium, Eucarya acuminata.*
Anogeissus leiocarpus, Khaya senegalensis, Parkia clappertoniana, Apophyullium anomalum, Atalaya hemiglauca, Atriplex nummularium, Brachychiton diversifolium, B. gregorii, Casuarina decaisneana, C. cristata, C. luehmannii, Eucalyptus flocktoniae.

Opuntia species are grown in plantations in the north of Argentina and in north-west Brazil for cattle food.

SPECIES MAINLY SUITED TO DRY, SANDY SOILS

BOTANICAL NAME	POPULAR NAME	REMARKS
Atriplex nummularia et al.	Salt bushes	Thrive in arid areas or on sandy dry soils
Barringtonia racemosa	Mudilla	Suited to damper sandy places
Calotropis gigantea	Milkweed	Common on sand
Canavalia obtusifolia	Seaside sword bean	Creeping leguminous perennial. Edible after boiling
Cassia auriculata	Matara tea	Large shrub, with edible pods. Medicinal
Casuarina equisetifolia	She-oak	Tolerates saline ground
Desmodium triflorum et al.		Small leaved clover-like perennials, suited to dry rocky localities
Euphorbia tirucalli	Milk hedge	Quick growing. Poisonous
Ipomoea biloba	Mudu	Creeping herb
Pandanus odoratissimus	Screw pine	Spreading bush with aerial shoots which descend and fix the plant in sand
Scaevola koenigii	Takkada	Large spreading bush
Tamarix gallica et al.	Tamarisks	Specially adapted to dry regions and sandy land
Tephrosia purpurea	Pila	Leguminous perennial
Thevetia nereifolia	Yellow oleander	Well suited to dry areas. Large shrub
Zizyphus spina-christi	Crown of thorns	Makes good hedges

These species are suitable for afforestation and ground cover on bare land, mainly in warmer regions. Numerous other types of trees and shrubs can be used for plantings, once some initial cover has been established, the choices depending upon climatic factors usually, provided additional considerations are satisfied. *Poisonous kinds should not be established within feeding or grazing areas where livestock are kept.*

Appendix II
Grasses and Herbage

THERE ARE many types of excellent high-yielding grasses and herbage plants suitable for providing pasturage and extra fodder between or around trees on forest farms. Selection should follow normal agricultural practice except that it pays wherever possible to use local species of indigenous origin. In the majority of cases, once land has been freed from useless scrub the native grasses will rapidly increase their output and spread quickly. If deficient in nutritional value or requiring supplementation, additional exotics can be sown as long as they have been chosen with care to suit the particular climatic and soil conditions.

Grasses normally fall into different classes: those adapted for fodder purposes, others ideal for grazing and some useful for conservation and reclamation tasks. However, certain species combine two or more of these qualities. For feeding purposes it is necessary to take into account such matters as moisture availability, compatibility, nitrogen level, digestibility, palatability, and related factors. The standard of production is also vitally important. The merits of different species and varieties can be assessed by drawing up a short table like this:

	Characteristics		
(Species arranged in order of merit)	PALATABILITY	DIGESTIBILITY	AGGRESSIVENESS
	Timothy	Tetraploid rye-grass	Diploid ryegrass
	Tetraploid rye-grass	Diploid ryegrass	Tetraploid ryegrass
	Diploid ryegrass	Meadow fescue	Cocksfoot
	Meadow fescue	Timothy	Timothy
	Cocksfoot	Cocksfoot	Meadow fescue
	Tall fescue	Tall fescue	Tall fescue
	Sainfoin	White clover	White clover
	White clover	Red clover	Red clover
	Red clover	Sainfoin	Sainfoin
	Lucerne (alfalfa)	Lucerne (alfalfa)	Lucerne (alfalfa)

Such comparisons do not, of course, show whether any particular
type will succeed in an area, since that depends upon appraisal of
its additional characteristics and responses in the field. There are
numerous species and cultivars or hybrids available, so the choice
is very wide.

GRASS SPECIES

NAME	REMARKS
Acroceras macrum, Nile grass	Rhizomatous and water-loving
Agropyron cristatum, Russian wheat	Creeping rhizomes, fairly drought-resistant
Agropyron distichum, sea wheat	Rhizomatous, hardy, but coarse
Agropyron, quack grass	Strong rhizomes, hardy
Agropyron smithii, western wheat grass	Creeping, deep-rooted and quick-growing, drought-resistant
Agrostis stolonifera, red top	Creeping, frost- and drought-resistant
Agrostis tenuis, New Zealand brown top	Prefers moist and cool areas
Ammophila arenaria, marram grass	Extensive creeper, good on sand
Andropogon appendiculatus	Rhizomatous, likes wetter land
Andropogon furcatus, bluestem	Vigorous and drought-resistant
Andropogon geradi, big bluestem	Deep-rooted, drought-resistant, but tolerant of some moist areas
Andropogon halapense, Cuba grass	Creeping rhizomes and edible seeds
Andropogon halli, sand bluestem	Rhizomatous, drought-resistant, grows on poor soils
Andropogon pertusus, Barbados sour grass	Heavy yielder, tolerates frequent cutting, suited to poorer land
Andropogon sorghum, Sudan grass	Tall, heavy yielder, but not quite as strong as Cuba grass; annual
Andropogon scoparius, little bluestem	Deep-rooted and hardy
Anthepora pubescens	Drought-resistant, grows in sand
Anthistiria australis, kangaroo grass	Subtropical
Anthistiria cymbaria, karawata	Subtropical, higher ground
Aristida amabilis	Drought-resistant, grows in sand
Aristida brevifolia	Very drought-resistant
Aristida namaquensis	Drought-resistant, thrives on sandy ground
Aristida obtusa	Very drought-resistant; palatable

NAME	REMARKS
Aristida sabulicola	Robust and drought-resistant
Aristida uniplumis	Grows in warm semi-desert areas
Arundo donax, Spanish reed	Rhizomatous and water-loving
Astrelba pectinata, Mitchell grass	Drought-resistant; good pastures
Axonopus compressus, carpet grass	Stoloniferous and hardy
Beckeropsis uniseta, silky grass	Creeping rhizomes, prefers moist and shady places
Brachiaria marlothii	Stoloniferous, likes moist, but tolerates some dry periods
Brachiaria mutica	Spreads rapidly, likes moist places
Brachiaria species, Tanner grasses	Strong, extensive creepers, but needs moist sites
Bromus inermis, smooth brome	Vigorous, with creeping rhizomes; will tolerate poorer soils; hardy
Bromus unioloides, prairie grass	Needs moist heavy soils
Bouteloua gracils, blue grass	Drought-resistant, grows on poor land
Boutenloua curtipendula, side-oat grama	Hardy for arid areas
Bouteloua eriopoda, black grama	Hardy for arid areas
Bouteloua hirsuta, hairy grama	Hardy for arid areas
Buchloë dactyloides, buffalo grass	Stoloniferous, deep-rooted, and quite drought-resistant
Cenchrus ciliaris, blue buffel	Drought-resistant, grows in sandy and stony soils
Chloris gayana, Rhodes grass	Stoloniferous, vigorous and drought-resistant, but cannot tolerate poor soils indefinitely
Chrysopogon aciculatus, love grass	Prefers moister districts
Coix lacryma-jobi, Job's tears	Suits warm areas with adequate moisture, or summer months in colder regions; often ranked as a cereal
Crysopogon montanus	Strong rhizomes, drought-resistant, suited to stony ground
Cynodon dactylon, Bermuda grass	Hardy, aggressive, and very adaptable
Cynodon plectostachyus, star grass	Robust and drought-resistant
Dactylis glomerata, cocksfoot	Drought-resistant to some extent; also tolerates poorly drained land; robust and leafy
Dactyloctenium australe, coast grass	Stoloniferous, frost- and drought-resistant, tolerates shade

NAME	REMARKS
Desmodium heterophyllum, maha	Thrives up to 2,000 feet above sea level in tropics; perennial herb
Digitaria diversinervis, Richmond grass	Stoloniferous and tolerant of shade
Digitaria pentzil, woolly finger-grass	Stoloniferous, hardy; covers bare ground
Digitaria scalarum	Rhizomatous, hardy, difficult to eradicate once established
Digitaria abyssinica	Rhizomatous
Digitaria seriata	Very drought-resistant, suits sandy soils
Digitaria smutsii	Drought-resistant and creeping habit
Digitaria swazilandensis, Swazi finger-grass	Creeping habit, hardy
Echinocloa pyramidalis, antelope grass	Robust, suits wet areas
Ehrharta gigantea, pyp grass	Rhizomatous, tall, drought-resistant
Ehrharta villosa	Grows on pure sand
Ehrharta calycina	Tall and also frost- and drought-resistant
Eleusine indica	Suits low and medium tropical elevations; annual
Elymust tritcoides, beardless wild rye	Quick-growing, likes cool areas
Elymust canadensis, wild rye-grass	Quick-growing, likes cool areas
Elymust glaucus, blue wild rye	Quick-growing, likes cool areas
Eragrostis abyssinica, Teff	Suits dry regions; annual
Eragrostis chloromelas	Hardy, suits drier areas, but can tolerate some wet conditions
Eragrostis curvula	Hardy, suits drier areas
Eragrostis tenella	Thrives in low tropical areas; annual
Eriochloa michauxii	Spreads rapidly, prefers moist soils
Euchlaena luxurians, Teosinte	Suits warm areas, if adequate water available. Prolific yielder
Festuca pratensis	Resistant to some drought, as well as cold, tolerates wetness
Festuca arundinacea, tall fescue	Resistant to some drought
Hemarthria altissima, swamp couch	Rhizomatous, spreads rapidly, hardy and moisture-loving

NAME	REMARKS
Heteropogon contortus	Quick-growing and hardy, suits drier conditions
Hilaria belangeri, curly mesquite	Very drought-resistant, strong roots
Hilaria jamesii, galleta grass	Very drought-resistant
Hilaria mutica, tobosa grass	Very drought-resistant
Holcus lanatus, Yorkshire fog	Moisture-loving; suits cold winters
Hyparrhenia aucta	Robust and hardy; tolerates wet
Hyparrhenia cymbaria, boat grass	Rhizomatous and moisture-loving
Hyparrhenia hirta, thatch grass	Drought-resistant, tufted
Imperata cylindrica, cotton-wood grass	Tough and adaptable, but prefers moister conditions
Ischaemum arcuatum	Rhizomatous; aggressive and moisture-loving
Ischaemum brachyatherum	Rhizomatous and moisture-loving, prefers heavy soil
Ischaemum ciliare, rattana	Tropical, but fairly tolerant of rainfall
Ischaemum muticum	Tropical
Ischaemum timorense	Suits damp and shady places, noted for its aerial roots
Justicia procumbens, mayani	Prefers moist areas, and grows amongst other species; herb
Leersia hexandra, rice grass	Rhizomatous and moisture-loving
Lolium perenne, perennial rye-grass	Frost-resistant with strong roots; good for winter use
Melinis minutiflora, molasses grass	Subtropical; repellent to tsetse
Miscanthidium sorghum, tambootie	Robust and moisture loving
Panicum coloratum	Stoloniferous and drought resistant
Panicum burmanni, Pagister grass	Grows mainly on wet land, prolific
Panicum curvatum	Suits warm moist areas
Panicum crusgalli (var.), cockspur grass	Both temperate and tropical varieties; good fodder
Panicum compositus	Suits shady places in warm tropics
Panicum muticum, Mauritius grass	Spreads rapidly in moist ground
Panicum lanipes	Grows in dry places with underground water; hardy
Panicum maximum, Guinea grass	Hardy and heavy yielding, needs adequate water and manuring in warm areas
Panicum prostratum	Suits drier districts

NAME	REMARKS
Panicum repens, couch grass	Tolerant of conditions, will withstand both wet and drought to a large extent; difficult to eradicate
Panicum spectabile, African wonder grass	Prefers moist localities; spreads rapidly once established
Panicum virgatum, switch grass	Extensive roots, drought-resistant
Panicum obtusum, vine mesquite	Extensive roots, drought-resistant
Paspalum dilatatum, Golden Crown	A low spreading species, drought- and frost-resistant; likes moist conditions
Paspalum conjugatum	Suited to moist shady places in warm areas
Paspalum distichum	Vigorous, likes moisture, but can resist some drought
Paspalum longiflorum	Resists drought well; a good coloniser
Paspalum notatum	Rhizomatous, short and aggressive
Paspalum obtusifolium	Suits moist shade under trees in warmer regions
Paspalum scrobiculatum, amu; koda millet	Resists drought well, and will thrive up to 6,000 feet above sea level in the tropics
Paspalum sanguinale, guruwal	Often considered as a cereal; suited to warmer regions
Paspalum urvillei, vasey grass	Frost-resistant, likes moisture
Paspalum vaginatum	Prefers saline soils and sand
Paspalum virgatum, upright paspalum	Suited to medium and high elevations in the tropics, or for subtropical areas
Pennisetum cencrhoides, congayam grass	Thrives in dry districts
Pennisetum clandestinum, kikuyu grass	Rhizomatous, vigorous, prefers reasonably moist conditions, but can withstand some drought
Pennisetum haareri, swamp Napier grass	Grows in water along stream banks or gullies; good fodder
Pennisetum purpureum, elephant grass	Drought-resisting, but likes some moisture, or more fertile soils
Pennisetum typhoideum, Napier grass	Withstands drought well; tall species
Poa nevadensis	Extremely drought-resistant
Poa secunda	Extremely drought-resistant

NAME	REMARKS
Phalaris arundinacea, reed canary grass	Frost-resistant; for winter grazing
Phalaris tuberosa, Canary grass	Frost- and drought-resisting, grows on poor soils
Phalaris stenoptera	Suits cold conditions
Phragmites communis, common reed	Aquatic and very tolerant; can resist drought and frost; grows in sand
Phragmites mauritianus	Tropical, suited to sandy places of varied kinds near water
Poa compressa, Canada bluegrass	Tolerates poor soils, and can resist some heat and drought
Poa pratensis, Kentucky bluegrass	Needs fertile land and moisture; unsuited to hot places; frost-resistant
Puccinellia maritima, sea poa	Drought- and frost-resistant, will stand saline and sandy conditions
Ruellia ringens, nilpuruk	Herb, often found amongst pastures in low elevations in the tropics
Schmidtia bulbosa, sand quick-grass	Stoloniferous, rapid spreader, frost- and drought-resistant
Setaria macro stachya, Plains bristle grass	Very adaptable and drought-resisting
Setaria sphacelata, kazungula	Robust and drought-resistant
Sorghum alumum, Columbus grass	Drought-resistant and tall-growing
Sorghum saccharatum, sweet sorghum	Cultivated for fodder, yielding first cutting at two and a half months after sowing
Spartina pectinata, sloughgrass	Grows in waterlogged land, especially tidal and muddy salt marshes
Spartina townsendii	Tough, suited to marshy ground
Spinifex squarrosus, water pink	Hardy, grows in sand
Sporobolus diander	Common in the hot tropics
Sporobolus fimbriatus	Drought-resistant, thrives in poor soils
Sporobolus smutsii	Stoloniferous, hardy, suited to sandy ground
Sporobolus tenellus	Rhizomatous, likes moist sandy soils
Sporobolus virginicus, beach drop-seed grass	Drought-resistant, but stands wet conditions, tolerant of saline areas

NAME	REMARKS
Stenotaphrum complanatum	Thrives under partial shade and has creeping habit; subtropical
Stenotaphrum americana, pimento grass	Subtropical, prefers shade
Stenotaphrum secundatum, seaside quick-grass	Prefers sandy soil, hardy, good winter grazing
Stipa comata, needle grass	Hardy, withstands frost and snow
Stipa spartea	
Stipa namaquensis	Very drought-resistant, grows on dry sandy soils
Themeda australis, kangaroo grass	Hardy, covers ground rapidly
Themeda triandra, blue grass	Tolerates a wide range of conditions; use with care since is often pyrophorous
Tricholaena rosea, red-top grass	Subtropical; seeds freely
Urochloa stolonifera	Grows in sandy soils near water
Zoisia macrantha	Stoloniferous, drought-resistant and succeeds on sand

Most of the species mentioned above are perennial in habit unless otherwise stated. Before finally deciding upon any particular types, advice should be sought from local agricultural advisory services regarding their suitability for the area in question, especially as far as factors like heat, rainfall and soils are concerned. The list is not exhaustive.

Appendix III
Oil-Producing Eucalypts

THE FOLLOWING list contains the names of some little known oil-producing species of eucalypts, as well as those of the popular and extensively used types.

A. MACRANTHERAE

E. baileyana. Bailey's Stringybark. A very good all-round tree for subtropical culture. Prefers poor sandy soils containing ironstone gravel. Yields 0.84 per cent oil.

E. tessellaris. Carbeen. Suitable for tropical forestry. Kino contains 53.2 per cent tannin, arabin and metarabin 5.5 per cent. Oil yield 0.16 per cent.

E. calophylla. Marri or red gum. Prefers laterite gravelly soil. Oil yield about 0.25 per cent.

E. trachyphloia. White bloodwood. Likes sandy soils with light clay subsoils, in dry hot districts. Yields 0.20 per cent oil.

E. gummifera. Bloodwood. A hardy and widely distributed coastal species, tolerates sandy soils or deep loamy sand. Oil yield about 0.07 per cent.

E. intermedia. Pink bloodwood. Tolerates considerable rainfall. Yields 0.14 per cent oil.

E. eximia. Yellow bloodwood. Grows on poor coastal sandstone and in rocky soils. Oil yield 0.46 per cent.

E. citriodora. Lemon-scented spotted gum. Fairly tolerant of conditions. Average oil yield 0.90 per cent but may give as much as 1.5 per cent from fresh leaves and 3 to 4 per cent from dry ones. Citronella content of the oil is 70 to 85 per cent.

E. maculata. Spotted gum. A fine coast range species, quite tolerant of soils. Yields 0.23 per cent of oil.

E. diversicolor. Karri. Prefers deep loamy soils. Rapid grower. Yields up to 1.2 per cent of oil.

E. grandis. Toolur. Suitable for coastal forestry. Oil yield is 0.27 per cent.

E. saligna, Sydney blue gum. Prefers heavier soils with good drainage. Oil yield about 0.13 per cent.

E. deanei. Deane's gum. Likes sandstone and granite slopes. The oil yield is generally 0.60 per cent.

E. botryoides. Bangalay. Thrives on subsaline areas and moist alluvial soils. Yields 0.12 per cent of oil. *E. Botryoides,* var. *Lyneii,* very similar.

E. robusta. Swamp mahogany. Likes saline areas near the coast. Yields 0.17 per cent oil.

E. resinfera. Red mahogany. Excellent for light sandy soils in sheltered positions with moderate rainfall. Oil yield is about 0.45 per cent.

E. kirtoniana. Bastard mahogany. Useful tree for mud flats, in moist saline places. Yields 0.26 per cent of oil.

E. pellita. Large-fruited red mahogany. Thrives in light well-drained sandy soils. Yields 0.38 per cent oil.

E. pumila. Mallee grey gum. Suits clay soils. Yields 1.65 per cent of oil.

E. propinqua. Small-fruited grey gum. Occurs both on slightly clayey and sandy loam soils. Good for subtropical forestry. Oil yield is about 0.25 per cent.

E. punctata. Grey gum. Suits poor rocky sandy soils and tolerates exposed positions. Oil yield is 0.82 per cent average.

E. longifolia. Woollybutt. Suits deep alluvial land. Oil yield is about 0.55 per cent.

E. cosmophylla. Cup gum. Suits drier conditions. Oil yield is 0.63 per cent.

E. cornuta. Yate. Common on gravelly loam soils. The oil yield averages 1.25 per cent.

E. lehmanni. Bushy yate. Very adaptable species. The oil yield is 0.86 per cent.

E. gomphocephala. Tuart. Likes sandy loam overlying limestone. Oil yield 0.04 per cent.

E. platypus. Round-leaved moort. Favours low hills and sandy loam flats with adequate moisture in soil. Useful for tanning. Oil yield is about 0.83 per cent.

E. occidentalis. Swamp or flat-topped yate. Prefers clayey loam soils. Oil yield is 0.96 per cent.

E. wandoo. Wandoo. (*E. redunca,* var. *elata.*) Likes granite with clay subsoil. Oil yield is 1.25 per cent, and the bark provides tannin.

E. dumosa. Congo mallee. Suits dry, barren and sandy wastes. Yields at least 1.00 per cent of oil.

E. angulosa. Ridge-fruited mallee. Likes dry conditions. Oil yield is about 0.90 per cent.

E. exserta. Bendo. Prefers sandy and basaltic soils. Oil yield is 0.83 per cent.

E. morrisii. Grey mallee. Likes semi-arid places. Yields 1.60 per cent of oil.

E. umbellata. Forest red gum. Useful for subtropical and tropical work. Oil yield is 0.6 per cent.

E. amplifolia. Cumbora or cabbage gum. Suits shallow alluvial soils with heavy clay subsoil. Oil yield is about 0.10 per cent.

E. dealbata. Tumble down gum. Grows best on well drained slopes. Yields 0.86 per cent of oil.

E. parramattensis. Calgaroo. Likes sandy soil with clay subsoil or poor alluvial land. Yields 0.57 per cent oil.

E. seeana. Narrow-leaved cabbage gum. Prefers well drained acidic sandstone and poor granite soils. Yields 0.80 per cent of oil.

E. bancrofti. Orange gum. Common on sandy soils and granite, often at higher elevations. Yields 0.55 per cent oil.

E. rudis. Moitch. Likes warm and moist situations. Yields about 1.20 per cent oil.

E. ovata. Swamp gum. Likes sandy flats with clay subsoils and swampy land. Tolerates moderately cool areas. Yields 0.25 per cent of oil.

E. camphora. Broad-leaved sally. Likes very cold and damp situations. Yields 1.35 per cent oil.

E. aggregata. Black gum. Useful on fresh-water marshy flats, at high elevations. Yields 0.05 per cent of oil.

E. acaciaeformis. Wattle-leaved peppermint. Suits clay soils. Oil yield is 0.20 per cent average.

E. parvifolia. Small-leaved gum. Tolerates poorer soils. Oil yield is about 0.75 per cent.

E. maculosa. Red spotted gum. Likes acidic sandstone and granite soils. Oil yield is 1.15 per cent.

E. angophoroides. Apple-topped gum. Likes granite and sedimentary deposits. Oil yield is 0.20 per cent.

E. stuartiana. But but. Likes alluvial flat lands. Oil yield is about 0.70 per cent.

E. elaeophora. Bundy. Suits poor slaty and granite soils. Yields 0.75 per cent of oil.

E. rubida. Candle-bark tree. Prefers alluvial flats and granite soils, at higher elevations. Oil yield is 0.07 per cent.

E. dalrympleana. Broad-leaved kindlingbark. Suits higher lands on basaltic and granite soils. Yields about 0.50 per cent oil.

E. irbyi. Irby's gum. Subtropical. Yields 0.15 per cent of oil.

E. gunnii. Cider gum. Suits subalpine conditions. Yields 0.70 per cent of oil.

E. urnigera. Urn-fruited gum. Likes cooler climates. Oil yield averages 1.15 per cent.

E. perriniana. Round-leaved snow gum. Suits high elevations. Yields 1.10 per cent of oil.

E. cordata. Heart-leaved silver gum. Likes low elevations in cool climates. Yields 2.35 per cent of oil.

E. pulverulenta. Silver-leaved mountain gum. Grows on slate and mica formations. The oil yield is about 2.25 per cent.

E. megacarpa. Bullich. Prefers swampy land and moist sandy loam soils, near coastal areas. Yields about 0.50 per cent of oil.

E. bicostata. Eurabbie. Likes moderately heavy soils and higher mountainous regions. Yields 0.95 per cent of oil.

E. maideni. Maiden's gum. Suits medium elevations, good for afforestation purposes. Yields about 1.00 per cent of oil.

E. goniocalyx. Spotted mountain gum. Prefers poorer but deep sandy soils. Yields about 1.00 per cent of oil.

E. vernicosa. Varnished-leaved gum. Suits subalpine places. Yields 0.80 per cent oil.

E. johnstoni. Johnston's gum. Also likes subalpine conditions. Yields about 1.30 per cent oil.

E. baeuerleni. Baeuerlen's gum. Subtropical at higher elevations. Yields about 0.35 per cent of oil.

E. quadrangulata. Soft white box. Likes volcanic or basaltic soils. Subalpine. The oil yield is 0.70 per cent.

E. macarthuri. Camden woolly butt. Prefers heavy alluvial land. Yields 0.21 per cent oil of fine odour.

E. smithii. Blackbutt peppermint. Suits alluvial flat land and volcanic areas. The oil yield is about 1.80 per cent.

E. viminalis. Ribbon gum. Suits mountain valleys. The oil yield is about 0.55 per cent.

E. cinerea. Argyle apple. Subtropical. The oil yield is about 1.20 per cent.

E. nova-anglica. New England peppermint. Subtropical. Yields 0.52 per cent of oil.

E. intertexta. Gum-barked coolabah. Suits semi-arid regions. Yields 0.20 per cent of oil.

B. Renantheroideae

E. diversifolia. Soap mallee. Suits moderately dry regions, and poorer sandy soils on limestone. Oil yield is about 0.42 per cent.

C. Renantherae

E. marginata. Jarrah. Thrives in ironstone gravelly soils. The oil yield is 0.25 per cent.

E. muelleriana. Yellow stringybark. Likes stiff, rather moist clay soils at low elevations. The oil yield is 0.90 per cent.

E. umbra. Bastard mahogany. Suits saline flats near the sea, and salt ridges, doing best in mildly salt-laden air. The oil yield is 0.60 per cent.

E. carnea. Thick-leaved mahogany. Subtropical. Yields 0.17 per cent of oil.

E. microcorys. Tallow wood. Suits rich loamy land with good rainfall near the coast. Yields 0.52 per cent of oil.

E. wilkinsoniana. Small-leaved stringybark. Likes subtropical coastal districts. Yields 0.98 per cent of oil.

E. laevopinea. Silver-to stringybark. Flourishes in elevated and sheltered positions. Yields 0.62 per cent oil.

E. macrorrhyncha. Red stringybark. Suits acidic poor soils. Yields 0.30 per cent oil.

E. blaxlandi. Blaxland's stringybark. Likes sheltered ridges and higher areas of sandy or granite soils. Yields 0.85 per cent of oil.

E. alpina. Grampians stringybark. Alpine. Yields 0.36 per cent of oil.

E. capitellata. Brown stringybark. Thrives on sandy land, near the sea. Prefers sheltered positions. Yields 0.12 per cent oil.

E. ligustrina. Privet-leaved stringybark. Suits exposed places and very hardy. Oil yield is 0.15 per cent.

E. penrithensis. Bastard stringybark. Likes sandstone regions. The oil yield is 0.70 per cent.

E. laseroni. Laseron's stringybark. This tree thrives in moist and colder areas. Oil yield is 0.40 per cent.

E. obliqua. Messmate. Common in hilly country on good loam in sheltered sectors. Yields 0.70 per cent of oil.

E. fastigata. Cut tail. Suited to cool mountain valleys with fair and deep soils. Yields 0.12 per cent oil.

E. regnans. Giant gum. Also thrives in cooler areas, with adequate water and deep well drained loamy soils. Yields 0.90 per cent of oil.

E. gigantea. Gum-top stringybark ash. Suits high elevations. Subalpine. Yields average 1.80 per cent oil.

E. sieberiana. Mountain ash. Satisfactory on poorer sandy land, often over friable clay. Yields 0.50 per cent oil.

E. taeniola. White-topped ash. Similar to *E. sieberiana* and gives 0.68 per cent oil.

E. consideniana. Yertchuk. Thrives on poor siliceous soils. The oil yield is about 1.25 per cent.

E. planchoniana. Bastard tallow wood. Subtropical. Yields 0.05 per cent oil.

E. virgata. Yellow-top ash. Likes cold damp regions with sandy soils, or rocky sites. Yields 0.35 per cent oil.

E. oreades. Blue ash. Suited to good sandy soils at moderate elevations. The oil yield is 1.25 per cent.

E. fraxinoides. White ash. Thrives on light, well-watered soils of moderate elevations. The tree will withstand some wind and snow. Yields up to 1.00 per cent oil.

E. stricta. Blue Mountain mallee. A hardy species suited to mountain areas. Yields 0.50 per cent oil.

E. apiculata. Boree. Likes sandy soils. Yields 0.70 per cent of oil.

E. vitrea. White-top messmate. Prefers colder conditions, with light soils. Yields as much as 1.65 per cent of oil.

E. pauciflora. Cabbage gum. Withstands severe cold, as well as wind and snow. Alpine. Yields 0.70 per cent oil.

E. stellulata. Black sally. Likes light but moist soils and moderate elevations. The species will withstand frost and strong winds. Yields about 0.30 per cent oil.

E. moorei. Narrow-leaved sally. Subalpine. Yields 0.80 per cent of oil.

E. linearis. White peppermint. Suits poorer, light soils. The oil yield is 1.50 per cent.

E. lindleyana. River peppermint. Suits sheltered areas of quite moderate elevation. The oil yield is 1.70 per cent. Aromatic.

E. salicifolia. Black peppermint. Thrives in poor, light soils. The oil yield is 1.90 per cent. Aromatic.

E. radiata. Grey peppermint. Likes light sandy soils, with stiffer subsoils. Yields about 3.50 per cent of oil.

E. australiana. Australiana. Subtropical. The oil yield is about 4.0 to 4.5 per cent. It is rich in cineol and has no phellandrene.

E. dives. Broad-leaved peppermint. Suits poorer land and sandstones. The oil yield is up to 3.00 per cent.

E. coccifera. Mt Wellington peppermint. Subalpine. The oil yield is about 0.62 per cent.

E. tasmanica. Tall silver peppermint. Subtropical and temperate species. Oil yield is 1.45 per cent.

E. andrewsi. New England blackbutt. Likes poor granite soils at medium elevations. Oil yield is 1.30 per cent.

E. piperita. Sydney peppermint. Confined to sandy ground and cooler localities. Oil yield averages 0.80 per cent.

E.haemastoma. Scribbly gum. Well suited to very dry places. Yields 0.45 per cent of oil. *E. Haemastoma*, var. *Sclerophylla*, has an oil yield of 0.65 per cent.

E. micrantha, var. *signata*. Peppermint-leaved white gum. Subtropical, prefers better land. The oil yield is about 2.00 per cent, and it contains b.ª phellandrene 40 per cent and piperitone 40-50 per cent, as well as some piperitol.

E. rossii. White gum. Likes sandstone regions. The oil yield is 0.75 per cent.

D. PORANTHEROIDEAE

E. leptophylla. Slender-leaved white mallee. Grows on stiff red loam and clay soils. Oil yield is 1.45 per cent.

E. odorata. Peppermint box. Withstands dry conditions and droughts. The oil yield is 0.90 per cent.

E. fruticetorum. Blue mallee. Prefers sandy and clayey soils, in sub-tropical areas. The oil yields vary from 1.50 to 2.70 per cent.

E. viridis. Green mallee box. Suits clayey-loam soils and is remarkably drought resistant. The oil yield is about 1.20 per cent.

E. bicolor. River black box. Suits river flats, but can withstand drought. Oil yield is 0.90 per cent.

E. bosistoana. Bosisto's box. This species prefers mild climates and limestone formations or loamy soils with a heavier subsoil. Oil yield is about 1.00 per cent.

E. behriana. Broad-leaved mallee box. Suited to hot and dry districts. Yield of oil is 0.63 per cent.

E. hemiphloia. Grey box. Likes a moderate climate, neither too warm nor too cold and heavy clay soil, but can thrive in light soils with clay subsoil. Oil yield is 0.60 per cent.

E. albens. White box. Common on limestone and basaltic soils. Yields oil at the rate of 0.12 per cent.

E. coolabah. Coolabah. Common on black soil plains. Drought resistant. Yields 0.48 per cent of oil.

E. racemosa. Narrow-leaved ironbark. Suits varied conditions, but does best in moderately hot areas. Yields 0.16 per cent of oil.

E. staigeriana. Lemon-scented ironbark. Tropical. The oil yield is 2.50 per cent, of attractive scent.

E. siderophloia. Broad-leaved ironbark. Very adaptable as regards soil requirements. Oil yield is 0.07 per cent.

E. melanophloia. Silver-leaved ironbark. Thrives best on loamy soils or sandy clays. Very hardy, withstanding a good deal of cold. Oil yield is 0.12 per cent.

E. TERMINALES

E. paniculata. Grey ironbark. Likes shale and sandy loams. The oil yield is of the order of 0.10 per cent.

E. affinis. Bastard box. Subtropical. Yields 0.26 per cent oil.

E. sideroxylon. Mugga. Prefers sedimentary formations. Yields 0.65 per cent of oil.

E. leucoxylon. White ironbark. Likes heavier alluvial soils. The oil yield is about 0.80 per cent.

E. melliodora. Yellow box. Suits good alluvium and granite soils, at very moderate altitudes. The oil yield is about 0.88 per cent.

E. dawsoni. Slaty box. Prefers stony ridges. Tropical. Yields 0.20 per cent of oil.

E. polyanthemos. Red box. Grows on poorer lands, in moist or moderately dry regions. The oil yield amounts to 0.85 per cent.

E. baueriana. Blue box. Suits river flats and lime-containing loamy soils. The oil yield is about 0.30 per cent.

F. Graciles

E. calycogona. Gooseberry mallee. Fairly drought-resistant. Yields 1.00 per cent oil.

E. gracilis. Yorrell. Useful for arid and semi-arid places. The oil yield is about 0.95 per cent.

G. Micrantherae

E. cneorifolia. Kangaroo island narrow-leaved mallee. Suits arid coastal zones, with limestone soils. The oil yield is 1.80 to 2.00 per cent.

H. Platyantherae

E. squamosa. Scaly bark. Thrives on barren sandy soils. The oil yield is 0.60 per cent.

E. oleosa. Giant mallee. Drought-resistant, prefers red loam soils or sandy loam. The oil yield is about 1.15 per cent.

E. websteriana. Webster's mallee. Suits dry regions. The species is rich in oil, but no definite figures are available.

E. salmonophloia. Salmon gum. Suits good red clay soils. The oil yield is about 1.45 per cent.

E. salubris. Gimlet gum. Prefers semi-arid land. The oil yield is 1.40 per cent and the bark produces tannin.

NOTE:

The figures for oil yields given for the different species are average ones and may be subject to variation in local conditions. Moreover, improved and selected strains and varieties under plantation culture often exceed the average yields for the types in question.

Appendix IV
Measuring Devices

RAINFALL

RAINFALL IS measured by means of a pluviometer or raingauge. To calculate the number of cubic feet per acre, multiply the depth of rainfall in inches by 3630, or, to give the number of gallons per acre, by 22623.

RAINFALL IN INCHES	CUBIC FEET PER ACRE	GALLONS PER ACRE	TONS PER ACRE
1	3,630	22,623	101.1
2	7,260	42,270	202.2
3	10,890	67,905	303.3
4	14,520	90,492	404.4
5	18,150	113,174	505.5

1 cubic inch of water weighs 3/5 oz. 224 gallons of water weigh 1 ton.

TREE HEIGHT

To prepare a dendrometer for measuring the heights of trees, take a staff six feet in length, with a sharp point at one end. To the centre of this fix with screws a piece of board twelve inches square. Now nail a lath diagonally across the board, and attach a plumb line to the staff for obtaining the perpendicular. Have a piece of string available for attaching to a hook placed at the lower end of the diagonal lath.

To carry out the measurement, position the staff in the ground some distance from the tree so that with the plumb exactly perpendicular the diagonal lath points to the top of it, the sight being taken by placing the eye to the bottom of the lath. Then extend the sight line to the ground by means of the string. The point where this touches the ground level to the centre of the trunk at the base of the tree will represent the actual height of the subject.

TIMBER

Take the girth in inches at the middle, divide by four, then square the result. This gives the mean sectional area of the trunk. Multiply the product by the length of the log in feet, divide by 144, and the quotient is the sum of the contents in cubic feet. Where there is bark, an allowance should be made for it, usually varying from ½ to 1½ inches to every foot of quarter girth. If the total quarter girth is 24 inches with thick bark, a deduction of from 2 to 3 inches is necessary, the quarter girth being taken at 21 or 22 inches.

ROADS

One cube of road metal measures 18 feet at the base by 5 feet broad, and 2½ feet high at the centre. It is 14 feet in length along the top ridge. This is sufficient for metalling about 500 square feet of road surface.

SOIL TEMPERATURE

This can be measured by using a thermistor. The device consists of a small capsule containing a compound of which the electrical resistance falls quickly with increasing temperature. Thermistors can be left buried in the ground with only the leads projecting.

CAPILLARY POTENTIAL OF THE SOIL (pF)

A soil tensiometer is employed to determine the capillary potential of the soil. It is filled with water, and as soil dries it will tend to draw out moisture from the vessel until the suction force is balanced by the mercury column in the capillary tube. Two tensiometers, with different depths of placement, can provide information about water movement in the land, such as the penetration of rainfall, or the region being exploited by the roots of crops.

LIGHT INTENSITY

There are various exposuremeters available which are calibrated to give direct light readings. Light measurements in plantations are normally expressed as percentages of full light in the open.

EVAPORATION POWER OF AIR

By using tables from the readings of a wet and dry bulb thermo-meter it is possible to measure by derivation the saturation deficit, the result being in absolute terms. An atmometer gives the com-parative measure from assessing directly the rate of evaporation from an exposed surface. There are many types of atmometers, both for rapid determinations of water loss, and for determining the weight of water withdrawn over considerable periods.

POTOMETER

Potometers allow simultaneous measurement of transpiration and water uptake to be assessed. There are numerous designs available.

MANUAL LABOUR

A labourer should be able to complete the following tasks dur-ing an average working day:

Engaged in making planting holes: 110 to 150 holes, ac-cording to the nature of the ground.
Engaged in planting out: 250 to 300 young trees.
Making planting containers from grass or other materials: 150 containers.

STOCKING RATES

1 large beast (bull or cow) requires as much forage as 5 smaller animals (sheep or goats).

On first class pasture land one or two bullocks can be grazed rotationally on one acre of herbage. The poorer the grazing condi-tions, the lower the stocking rate will be, until rates of one beast to 20 or even 40 acres may be necessary (nomadic pastoral prac-tice). With tree crops in good condition, the collective produce may provide adequate feed for one, two or more large beasts per acre of bearing or fruiting surface, depending on output required.

Bibliography

BOOKS

Burkill I. H., *A Dictionary of the Economic Products of the Malay Peninsula*, 2 vols., Crown Agents for the Colonies, London, 1935.

Dallimore W., & Jackson A. B., 4th ed. revised by Harrison S. G., *A Handbook of Coniferae*, Edward Arnold, London, 1966.

Dalziel J. M., *The Useful Plants of West Tropical Africa*, Crown Agents for Overseas Governments and Administrations, London, 1955.

Engler A., & Drude O., *Die Vegetation der Erde*, 14 vols., Wilhelm Englemann, Leipzig, 1896-1928.

Hill A. F., *Economic Botany*, McGraw Hill, New York, 1952.

Kaul R. N., *Afforestation in Arid Zones*, W. Junk, The Hague, 1970.

Kramer P. J., & Kozlowski T. T., *Physiology of Trees*, McGraw Hill, New York, 1960.

Macmillan H. F., *Tropical Planting and Gardening*. Macmillan, London, 1946.

Puri G. S., *Indian Forest Ecology*, 2 vols., Oxford Book & Stationery Co., New Delhi and Calcutta, 1960.

Russell Smith J., *Tree Crops – A Permanent Agriculture*, Harcourt, Brace & Co., 1929.

Schnell R., *Plantes alimentaires et vie agricole de l'Afrique noire*, Editions Larousse, Paris, 1957.

Stamp L. Dudley, *Man and the Land*, Collins, London, 1955.

Sturtevant E. L., *Sturtevant's Notes on Edible Plants*, ed. by U. P. Hendrick, Report of the New York Agricultural Experiment Station, vol. 2, part 2, 1919.

Uphof J. C. Th., *Dictionary of Economic Plants*, H. R. Englemann, Weinheim, 1959.

Walter H., *Die Vegetation der Erde*, 2 vols., Gustav Fischer, Jena, 1962.

Woodbury A. M., *Principles of General Ecology*, Blakiston, New York, 1954.

PAPERS AND ARTICLES BY J. SHOLTO DOUGLAS

'Bold New 3-D Forestry Experiments in Northern Transvaal', *Veldtrust*, pp. 29-30, September-October, 1960, Johannesburg.

'Trees – Fodder for Man and Beast', *Farmer's Weekly*, October 18, pp. 31-3, 1961, Bloemfontein, Orange Free State.

3-D Forestry', *World Crops*, vol. 19, no. 4, September 1967, pp. 20-24, London.

'Land-rescue Agriculture: Three-dimensional Forestry', *Impact of Science on Society*, vol. XVIII, no. 1, pp. 5-25, United Nations Educational, Scientific, and Cultural Organisation, Department of Advancement of Science, Paris, 1968.

'Three-dimensional Forestry', *Science Journal*, vol. 4, no. 8, August 1968, London.

'Upandaji wa miti', *Ukulima wa Kisasa* (Tanzania), August 1968, Dar es Salaam.

'3-D Multiple-use Forest Projects', *Quarterly Journal of Forestry*, vol. LXIII, no. 1, January 1969, The Royal Forestry Society of England, Wales, and Northern Ireland, London.

'Farming the Forests: 3-D Forestry', *The Scottish Landowner*, October 1968, Edinburgh.

'Triple Harvest from Trees', No. 3 of *Features Newsletter* No. 41, Central Office of Information, London.

Forest farming: an ecological approach to increase nature's food productivity, United Nations Educational, Scientific and Cultural Organisation, Paris, France, April 1973.

MISCELLANEOUS

Various pamphlets and bulletins are issued from time to time by government departments, experimental or research stations, and other organisations on the growing of particular tree crops. Amongst magazines and journals, the following often contain useful information for tree farmers:

Commonwealth Forestry Review, Commonwealth Forestry Association, Northumberland Avenue, London W.C.2, England, U.K.

Farm Forestry, P.O. Box 2721, Wellington, New Zealand.

Quarterly Journal of Forestry, Royal Forestry Society, 49 Russell Square, London W.C.1, England, U.K.

Scottish Forestry, Royal Scottish Forestry Society, 7 Albyn Place, Edinburgh 2, Scotland, U.K.

Trees, Journal of the Men of the Trees Society, Stansted Park Estate Office, Rowlands Castle, Hants, England, U.K., or local branches.

Unasylva, Food and Agriculture Organisation of the United Nations, Via delle Terme di Caracalla, Rome, Italy.

Acknowledgements

J. S. D. wishes to express his indebtedness to the following persons for their help and support during field research. (In cases where they have passed away this acknowledgement records a grateful memorial of their assistance and advice.)

The Rev. Toyohiko Kagawa;

Lord J. Boyd-Orr, formerly Director-General of the Food and Agriculture Organisation of the United Nations;

Professor J. Russell Smith;

Dr Hugo Boyko, President of the World Academy of Art and Science; Chairman, International Commission for Applied Ecology (International Council of Scientific Unions in Cooperation with UNESCO, and Chief Ecologist, Israel;

Dr Elisabeth Boyko;

Dr W. F. Bewley, C.B.E., D.Sc., V.M.H., former Director of the Experimental and Research Station, Cheshunt;

Dr Eliot Coit;

and to the undernoted authorities:

National Botanic Gardens, Lucknow, Uttar Pradesh, India;

United States Department of Agriculture;

Royal Botanic Gardens, Kew, England;

Royal Botanic Gardens, Paradeniya, Sri Lanka;

Directorate of Forestry, Pretoria, South Africa;

Division of Horticulture, Pretoria, South Africa;

Colonial Products Laboratory and Advisory Bureau, London;

Division of Botany, South Africa;

Citrus and Sub-Tropical Horticultural Research Station, Nelspruit;

Department of Forestry, Southern Rhodesia;

University of South Africa;

Federal Ministry of Agriculture, Salisbury, Rhodesia;

Department of Irrigation, South Africa;

Departments of Agriculture and Forestry, Hilo, Hawaii;

Ministry of Agriculture, Dar es Salaam, Tanzania;

Department of Forestry, Limbe, Malawi;

Department of Agriculture, Nicosia, Cyprus;

Forest Research Institute, Kepong, Malaysia;

Department for the Advancement of Science, United Nations Educational, Scientific and Cultural Organisation, Paris;

Department of Agriculture, Government of West Bengal;

and a number of others.

Enquiries for further information on agri-silviculture from readers may be addressed to:

J.Sholto Douglas,
c/o Watkins,
Bridge Street,
Dulverton,
Somerset,
England

Comments and information on work in progress will also be welcomed.

ADDENDA

The publishers wish to acknowledge with thanks Miss Wendy Campbell-Purdie's permission to quote from her book *Woman Against the Desert* (London: Gollancz, 1967).

page 5   The examples of annual yields mentioned refer to the conditions noted in the text. Less favourable circumstances or quality of trees will result in lower production.

page 21 lines 13-33   The original comments upon which these passages are based were kindly supplied by Miss W.Campbell-Purdie to the author J.S.D. some years ago and appeared in *Blueprint*, the Appendix to the book *Woman Against the Desert*, written jointly by her and Lord Fenner Brockway. (Publisher: Victor Gollancz Ltd., London 1967.) More detailed and recent evidence on the general expansion of the Sahara Desert, compiled by the United Nations Organization, indicated that in certain regions, such as the northern Sudan, the zone of aridity and desiccation has spread outwards by as much as 200 kilometres during the past twenty years.

page 142 lines 4-6   The Chinese bamboo referred to here is not the same species as those tested in Ireland and noted in the preceding sentences. It is a warmth-loving type and its attributes are recorded as a matter of interest only, since it would need protection in colder localities.

Index